W9-ATL-643

FOUNDATIONS
For the
LIFE SCIENCES
Second Edition

Harvey Workman

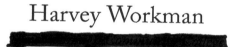

McGraw Hill **Custom Publishing**

Boston Burr Ridge, IL Dubuque, IA Madison, WI New York San Francisco St. Louis
Bangkok Bogotá Caracas Lisbon London Madrid
Mexico City Milan New Delhi Seoul Singapore Sydney Taipei Toronto

FOUNDATIONS FOR THE LIFE SCIENCES

McGraw-Hill's Custom Publishing consists of products that are produced from camera-ready copy. Peer review, class testing, and accuracy are primarily the responsibility of the author(s).

11 12 13 14 15 16 17 18 19 20

ISBN-13: 978-0-07-288160-8
ISBN-10: 0-07-288160-7

Editor: Ann Jenson
Production Editor: Nina Meyer
Printer/Binder: Quebecor World

Acknowledgement

This book could not have been completed without the unending dedication of friend and colleague, Dwight Meyer. His developing the computer generated illustrations, along with acting as a professional peer sounding board, were invaluable. Acknowledgement is also given to Sylvia Graham and Marilyn Braun For their pioneering efforts in this course. Their early text was a guiding light, helping to foster the writing of this book.

Table of Contents

THE PREFACE

There are new college students out there, many in great need of remediation. The problem is being addressed in the areas of reading, writing, and mathematics, but not to the same degree in the sciences. Many students claim they had science courses in high school, but didn't learn very much. Many had these courses so long ago that they remember nothing of them. The days of biology courses teaching about plants and animals are behind us. College-level biology courses require fundamental knowledge of chemistry and physics before the student can put together an understanding of today's molecular based biology. This book was written to address this problem.

Today's science texts are voluminous; they try to keep up with current knowledge, which is growing exponentially. To our students in need of remediation these books are overwhelming. To get concepts across it was important for the author to take certain liberties in the writing of this book, such as simplification and generalization of certain concepts, and leaving out some material that would tend to complicate and make learning more difficult. The idea here, is for the students to leave this course with an overall literacy in the sciences, leading to a smooth transition into life science courses.

BRIDGING THE GAP BETWEEN HIGH SCHOOL AND COLLEGE

In secondary or high school you were probably asked to learn subject matter that your teacher went over and over again in class. The teacher required that you do homework on the same material after class to reinforce your learning. Then finally you were tested on the material, often you were asked to mimic or parrot what you memorized. If you passed these tests you were a successful high school student. Well, in college learning is different. You have to motivate yourself to learn and succeed on your own. Your professor will give you the information you need and usually won't repeat it numerous times, because of time constraints. Most professors don't give homework, and when they do test you, they are more interested in finding out if you understand the material and whether you can think, by integrating ideas you've learned, and solve problems related to the material. That type of test truly tells if you have a mastery of the subject matter.

HOW TO SUCCEED IN THIS COURSE BY UNDERSTANDING CONCEPT FORMATION

We learn by connecting things together. Building concepts is done in steps. To proceed, you must cement the ideas presented to you, to something you already have stored in your memory, let's call this a concept connector. It becomes very difficult if you have nothing to hang or connect the initial idea on, but if you do, it becomes a much easier task. We then proceed from one step to the next using these concept connectors building and building until the complete concept is formed and fully understood.

Learning Concepts

There is an old adage" learning is by doing". And it's true. To learn and retain concepts, the more things you do associated with the facts you are trying to learn, the easier it is to remember them. For example if you are trying to remember a sequence of numbers that you see on a piece of paper, start by writing the sequence down. Look at the sequence, say the sequence, listen to it repeated to you, and if you could, even smell it, or feel it. The more senses you get involved in the learning process the more pathways you could use in your brain to connect this sequence of numbers. This holds true for most things that you have to learn.

To illustrate how these concept connectors work let's look at the columns shown below. If you were asked to memorize the characters in column 1, in let's say 30 seconds, could you do it? No you can't. Why not?, because you have nothing to connect these symbols with. They have absolutely no meaning for you. Let's go over to the second column, these are symbols that you may recognize. Can you reproduce these on a piece of paper after studying this list for 30 seconds? I still doubt it! Now look at the third column. What makes this easier to remember? You got it, letters of the alphabet. You learned this at a young age and you therefore have a concept connection. It becomes easier in the next column because even though you don't know what meaning they have, these words can be sounded out, another concept connection, and another sense, easier still. In the next column the words can be said and have meaning, again because of more concept connections it's easier. No doubt in 30 seconds anyone can learn and remember this. In the last column these words are connected in a meaningful way. Our concepts can be learned instantly. This demonstration is very important because it shows that if you learn the basic concepts that are presented throughout this text, then you'll have the concept connectors required in place, and higher level courses will become more manageable to you. This becomes the basis for taking this course.

1	2	3	4	5	6
		TNBF	ZURB	BLUE	WANT
		VLBK	FLIM	SLAP	SOME
		GNLT	PURK	THEN	LOVE

BUILDING TERMINOLOGY

Polymorphonuclearacidophilicleucogranulocyte! Well, what is this? What does it mean? Let's find out!

A very powerful learning tool in the sciences is learning the needed vocabulary. This vocabulary building is based upon derivation of the word parts. These provide you with clues, which will help you, learn and remember the words. The word parts are referred to as roots, prefixes, and suffixes, depending on where they are found in the word. Prefixes are found at the front of the word, and suffixes at the end.

Examples: phil = to love, leuc = white, cyt = cell, morph = to change, or shape, granul =grains, nuclear = seed, or kernal, poly = many.

These word parts may also contain short connecting letters so that the entire word can be sounded out, and flow much better.

Example: cancer/ /to make
                   carcin/o/genic   In this case the connector is the letter "o".

Many of these scientific terms have their word parts described from right to left, like the word biology. This term doesn't mean life the study of. Instead we work from the back of the word to the front. Biology means the study of life.

In science most word parts have been derived from either the Greek or Latin. These word parts are literally defined from the ancient Greek or Latin, and many times can only give you a clue as to the modern-day, true meaning of the word, but they still act as the concept connector for you. Now let's go back to that long biological term that we mentioned at the beginning of this section. We attack it by dividing it up into all the word parts.

Poly/morph/o/nuclear/acid/o/phil/ic/leuc/o/granul/o/cyte

Now go back to the examples of word parts listed above and place the meanings below.

many/shaped/nucleus/acid/loving/white/granule containing/ cell.

See how easy that was! The word parts told you a great deal about this term. It's now much easier to remember this word.

The best way to build your biological vocabulary is to tackle a number of these word parts each day and try to make as many terms as you can out of them, these don't have to be real words. Then see if you can reverse the process by taking those words and see if you can recall what their word parts mean. Another way to study this vocabulary building is to scan through biology texts and simply copy down terms you are not familiar with. Dissect the terms into word parts, then go to the list of word parts that's in the back of this book and find their meanings. Put these meanings together to describe the term.

The average student won't do this! He or she must be motivated to do this work. I have the answer! Why don't we make this part of each test you take during the semester? Sure, that will work. You are now motivated to do this on your own. Good luck!

STUDY HABITS

Different studying methods work for different students: the method that seems to work best for most beginning students is to primarily listen and concentrate on understanding while your professor lectures. If there is something that you don't understand, ask. That's why the professor is there. Otherwise who needs professors, each student would simply be given a text and asked to read it and learn from it. When you are in class don't concentrate on note taking, instead record the lecture, using a tape recorder. When you get home, sit down with your tape recorder and notebook, and while listening to the lecture, formulate a good set of notes for that days lecture. What you are doing is listening for a second time, at your leisure. If you find a concept difficult to understand repeat the playing of that section over and over again till you understand it so that you can put it down on paper in your own words. Remember if you didn't understand it during the lecture you asked then! Learning takes effort on your part for a successful outcome. For every hour that you are in class, you should be spending two hours at home studying. When a test is announced and you study for it, try the following:

1. Take your notes covering the subject area you will be tested on, and make a short outline on a separate piece of paper. Include everything!

2. Condense your notes so that you have less volume to worry about.

3 using only the outline rewrite your condensed set of notes trying to leave out nothing. Go back and check your condensed set of notes to see if you were able to include everything. If not, study your notes again. Remember and try to use all the senses you can when studying.

4. Time to take a short break from study. Watch TV, go for a walk, eat something, call a friend, and try to completely forget the test coming up.

5. After your break, repeat the writing of your condensed notes while only seeing the outline. Check again to make sure everything is included.

6. Repeat steps 4 and 5 until you don't even need the outline, and your notes are firmly embedded in your brain.

When you're confident and sure that you are totally prepared for an examination, you'll find you don't freeze up on exams. You don't have to use the excuse " I studied the wrong material," because you studied all of the material. This technique works and it works well. Another great idea is a bunch of heads is better than one. Hook up with other students and form small study groups. If you are a good student, doing well in class, you will learn and study a lot better by teaching other students. This reinforces your learning and insures you a better grade.

One technique that works when you must memorize a list of facts is called mnemonics. This is where you take the sequence of facts you must learn and hook the first letter of each fact to words you are more familiar with, and it is possible to make phrases with sentences you will more easily remember.

Example: CHON'S CaP   = important elements found in man.

Carbon, Hydrogen, Oxygen, Nitrogen, Sulfur, Calcium, and Phosphorus.

TAKING TESTS

1. Make sure that you concentrate your thoughts only on taking the test when it's time to take it. This is easier said than done.

2. Finalize your studying the day and night before the test and make sure you eat well, hours before taking the test to give your body a chance to digest the food so that you have the energy available to think properly and remember all that you studied.

3. Make sure you don't stay up all night studying, but instead plan your study sessions so that you can get a good night's sleep before taking the exam. A well-rested body works best.

4. When given the exam, quickly scan all the questions so that you can see what will be asked of you, and you can budget your available time to properly take the test.

5. Answer specifically what is asked of you, and not all of what you know.

6. Good luck!

THE NATURE OF SCIENCE

Science is the systematic accumulation of a body of knowledge based on proven facts. It can be two things, the organized body of facts or the method used to unearth those facts. Science deals with the real world (reality), not imagination or creativity. That is why when a person writes a poem, an artist paints a picture, or a composer writes a song, it is not science. There are many forms of science. Those that deal with the natural world are called the natural sciences. These sciences deal with all natural objects and processes, living and nonliving that make up the natural world. Sciences can also be subdivided into the physical and life sciences depending on whether they deal with the physical or the living world

The major natural sciences are physics, chemistry, geology, biology, and astronomy. In physics we study matter and energy. In chemistry we study the composition of the matter. Geology studies the earth, astronomy the universe, and biology life. These sciences, are interdependent on one another. Thus overlaps occur, such as geophysics, physical chemistry, astrophysics, biophysics, geochemistry, astrochemistry, biochemistry, astrobiology and biogeology.

Applied science is when man changes nature. Applied science makes real what does not exist in the natural world. Thus medicine, nursing, engineering, dentistry, and physical therapy are all examples of applied science. All the applied sciences dealing specifically with man are known as social sciences. Sciences like sociology, psychology, history, philosophy, archeology, economics, and political science are examples of the social sciences.

Technology is the tools; machinery, apparatus and or the skills that allow applied science to change the natural world. Examples of technology would be bridges, computers, telephones, radios, stethoscopes, data processing, typing, and computer programming.

HOW SCIENCE WORKS

People are inquisitive and want to know all they can about the world around them. Historically science can be traced back to its beginnings when early man relied on superstition and primitive religion to guide him and help predict events. Many civilizations followed, and each added something to the advancement of science.

The ancient Greek civilization, with its great thinkers used observation and logical thinking to bring science to a new level. Aristotle was most famous amongst them. Through extensive observation he was able to divide all things in the natural world into four categories.

1.earth
2.air
3.water
4.fire

He also tried to classify things by dividing them into animal, vegetable, and mineral.

Using logic and observation, diseases at that time were thought to be caused by an imbalance between man's internal structure and the environment around him. By bringing these imbalances back to a perfect balance, disease could be eliminated. You see man was at the center of the Greek universe; even their gods took on the image of man. It was believed that the body humors or liquids could balance man's internal structures. Just think about it, if you are sick with a cold, we observe excess mucus causing a cough, sneezing, watery eyes, from a fever, excess perspiration. A urinary tract infection leads to increased flow of urine. A gut infection, diarrhea. Naturally it was thought that by increasing other body humors flow you could balance the body back to good health. So the most important drugs of the day became laxatives (increases the flow of feces). Emetics (causes vomiting). Diuretics (increases the flow of urine), and the like. Disease, it was thought was initially caused by an imbalance in man's external environment, which brought about the imbalance within man, or the disease state.

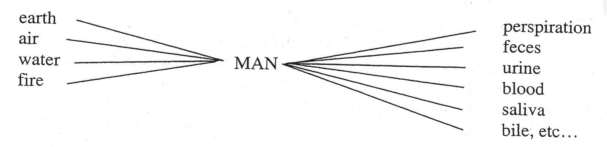

The famous Greek physician who became the father of medicine, Hippocrates, studied a disease which could cause chills and fever and was associated with marshy and swampy areas, in other words the external environment of man. The air was bad and smelled horribly in these areas. He called this disease bad air disease or malaria. Today scientists know it is caused by a one-celled animal, or protozoan called *Plasmodium*, and transmitted by a mosquito. So here you have it, by using creative thinking, logic, and careful observation the ancient Greeks thought they could get a handle on disease, but as you see with limited success.

Starting in the 1500's people started questioning more and more the explanations of the natural world that were passed on to them. It was from here that modern science and the scientific method began to be perfected, and became what it is today.

THE SCIENTIFIC METHOD

The scientific method is the general term for the way things are done in science. It is the very way that science sets about to answer questions about the natural world. It is based on systematic observation, questioning, reasonable explanation, and modification of concepts based on further observation. It is not a formula to be followed religiously. It all depends upon the questions asked and how they may be answered. Generally a typical format for how science is carried out looks like this:

1) OBSERVATION: Scientists begin by making observations about the phenomena or occurrences they are interested in learning about.

2) THE PROBLEM: The observations lead to questions or problems that the scientist wants answered. The scientist must be careful to pose his question in as precise a format as possible, otherwise it becomes too complex to work with. This problem or question must always end with a?

3) COLLECTION OF BACKGROUND INFORMATION: If the scientist is to do work in a specific area of science, he must learn all he can about this area. The same is true of the phenomenon he observed from step one. He must research the past work of scientists who already searched the same or similar problems. Look at the accepted references for the subject area. Search libraries and the Internet for the literature, studies, and reviews found within the area. Learn all he can about what he will be working with. The scientist may even want to do some preliminary experiments.

4) FORMING A HYPOTHESIS: It is now time to formulate a hypothetical answer to his initial question. This hypothesis should be based on the scientist's best educated guess. A hypothesis should always be in the form of a positive statement. An example follows:

Problem: Is the moon yellow?   Hypothesis: The moon is yellow!

5) TESTING THE HYPOTHESIS: This can be done many ways, conducting surveys, carrying out detailed observation, producing computer models, or most common, devising an experiment.

To set up the scientific experiment the scientist must consider first the method he will use. Then he must determine the materials and equipment that he will need to carry out his experiment. Finally he must consider setting up two groups. One group will be the control group. In this group all conditions will be as normal as possible. In the other group, the experimental group, all the conditions will be normal except one, the variable condition. This is the thing that the scientist wants to investigate. Now the two groups will be observed and compared on a regular basis all observations must be very carefully recorded. The recorded information is called the data. Any difference that is noted is assumed to be due to the variable condition. The careful study of the data is made and a conclusion is drawn based on the data. This is only a tentative conclusion that requires further verification before it can be accepted as the true statement about the reality of what exists in nature. One of the most important parts of conducting experiments is proper measurement. We will be spending some time on this later.

DRAWING A CONCLUSION: in order to draw a conclusion from his measurements, the scientist must interpret his data. The raw data, or the initial set of measurements for the experiment is usually impossible to interpret, unless it is put into a more meaningful form. The scientist can summarize the data by using the statistical approach. He uses such things as the mean or average, median, mode, standard deviation, and range, etc.
The use of charts and graphs is a very important method of condensing data and graphically illustrating it for the reader. There are different types of graphs available, for example bar, pie, and line graphs. The one that best presents the data should be chosen.

STANDARD RULES FOR MAKING GRAPHS

1) Make sure the title describes the subject matter best.
2) Always use the ruler and graph paper to plot the points accurately.
3) Space evenly all the intervals along both axes.
4) The y-axis is the vertical axis, and the x-axis is the horizontal axis.
5) Pick the minimum and maximum values so that the data extends over most of the graphs area.

The conclusion is considered tentative and requires further verification. If the conclusion to the experiment is found to support the original hypothesis, the scientist is not done, he repeats the experiment, or reports the work so that others can reproduce the results. Reproducibility is very important in conducting science.

FACT: If the verified hypothesis is accepted by the scientific community, and if it is added to the body of scientific knowledge as a single bit in a bigger puzzle, then it can be called a scientific fact.

THEORY: If the verified hypothesis or a series of verified hypotheses is very complex and describes a part of the natural world then it may be called a theory.

LAW: If the verified hypothesis or a series of verified hypotheses can accurately and mathematically describe and predict occurrences in nature, with the scientific community completely agreeing, then it becomes a scientific law.

All three of these that describe natural occurrences are not written in stone and are continuously open to further experimentation, and are subject to change. For this is the way that science works.

MODELS IN SCIENCE

When a scientific problem is very complex and too difficult for the scientist to deal with, he often will form a model or simpler representation of the problem. The model allows the scientist to more easily tackle the problem by testing, or using the model. Very often scientists and engineers will first produce models, such as cars, boats, airplanes, machines, factories, etc., then work to eliminate all the bugs in these models before building the real thing. These are referred to as physical models. Others are conceptual and computer models.

SYMBOLS IN SCIENCE

Often scientists use symbols. They are a shorthand for more difficult concepts. The scientist uses symbols all the time. Such things as numbers and the letters of the alphabet are symbols. The student may find the learning of these scientific symbols difficult at first because he or she must learn the symbol as well as what it stands for. Later when the symbol is used instead of what it stands for it will help the student in thinking and presenting scientific ideas in a more concise way.

Examples:

a. Two sodium atoms plus one diatomic chlorine molecule put together will yield two sodium chloride molecules and energy.

b. $2 Na + Cl_2 \rightarrow 2NaCl + \Delta G$

Now let's consider a concrete example of an experiment. Suppose you go to the doctor and the doctor tells you that your cholesterol level is to high and that because of this you must go on a low-fat diet. This means that you can no longer eat ice cream, cake, fried foods, bacon, and many other foods that you enjoy. You aren't too happy about this. You would like to be sure that the doctor is correct and that this is absolutely essential before you commit yourself to these deprivations. Clearly you want to know if a high fat diet really causes increased blood cholesterol. This is the problem. So, what can you do? Well, you can go to the library, or go on the Internet, and find out what cholesterol is. You can find out what kinds of experiments have been done in regard to the effects of high fat diets on blood cholesterol levels. You can also read about the relationship between cholesterol level and hypertension and heart disease. This would constitute the background of your experimental procedure.

The next step is to formulate your educated guess, your hypothesis based on the information that you learned in your library or Internet studies. A good hypothesis would be that a high fat diet leads to a high blood cholesterol level.

Now you must consider what materials and methods you will use in your experimental procedure. First of all you will need some animals to use in the experiment. You could use human beings but they are difficult to control. In general, human beings are not very cooperative. Since large numbers are required to make your experiment statistically valid, the use of human beings in the experiment is probably very impractical. Suppose, instead, you use 200 mice, 100 for the control group and 100 for the experimental group. Mice are relatively inexpensive and easy to care for. You can completely control their diet. Suppose you feed each control mouse five pellets of mouse food per day and unlimited water. Each mouse in the experimental group should get four pellets of mouse food per day, unlimited water plus half an ounce of cheese, a high fat food.

You must also have cages for the mice, equipment for taking daily blood samples and measuring the blood cholesterol level. It is important that all mice, both experimental and control, be kept In the same room, at the same temperature, light intensity, and humidity. It is equally important that we use the same numbers of males and females in each group and that the mice be the same age and be similar genetically, the same strain, that is the mice must be closely related.

The next thing to do is carry out the actual experimental procedure. That is you must keep the two groups of mice under as similar conditions as possible, but feed them different diets. Every day we must test the blood cholesterol level of each mouse and record this data carefully. This will probably have to be done for about a year in order to see any real difference or to decide that there is no difference between the blood cholesterol level of the experimental and the control groups.

What can we do with the data? A good way to handle data is to organize it into a table.

AVERAGE CHOLESTEROL LEVELS * VERSUS TIME		
DAY	CONTROL GROUP	EXPERIMENTAL GROUP
0	110	110
10	111	110
20	111	112
30	109	114
40	110	117
50	112	120
60	111	122
70	109	124

* mg = milligram = a unit of mass, ml = milliliter = a unit of volume.

Cholesterol levels are usually given in terms of mg/100 ml of blood.

A graph can also be used:

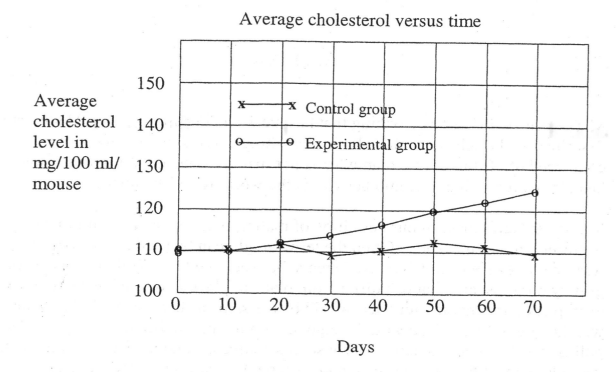

Note that even within the control group a slight fluctuation occurred, although both the table and the graph show a clear difference between the two groups.

The above data clearly leads to the conclusion that a high fat diet increases the blood cholesterol level, but note that this is only proof that this result was obtained in this case. In order to believe with some degree of certainty this is the true situation in all cases you must repeat the experiment many times. The results in this case may just be an accident. Repetition is very important if you want to believe that this is the truth all the time or at least most of the time. In addition, the experiment should be repeated with human beings, because although humans and mice are similar, obviously some physiological differences occur.

Only after several repeated experiments have been performed, is the conclusion believed to represent reality. Now the conclusion may reach the level of a theory. Note, we still believe that this is not an absolute truth for all animals. In summary this is the scientific method.

MATTER

Matter can be defined as anything that has mass and occupies space. Matter can be described as the substance that all physical things, living and nonliving are composed of. If this is true than what is not matter? The answer to this is love, hate, logic, reasoning, etc. in other words the workings of the mind.

We use the term mass in our definition of matter, mass is the amount of matter that is present in the substance. Often the term weight can be used interchangeably with mass. There is however a difference between the two. Weight is the effect of gravity on mass, and that can differ from place to place in our universe. For example, on the moon your mass would be the same as here on earth, but your weight would differ. You would weigh less on the moon, because the gravitational pull is less than here on earth. Because this course is conducted only on our planet, and relatively at the same altitude and latitude, we can use the two terms interchangeably.

We also used the term space in our definition. Space and volume are interchangeable terms. When we measure the length of an object we can say it is equal to X or one dimension. If we measure the area that the object takes up then we measure X times X which equals X^2 or two dimensions, very often length times width. Finally we measure the space taken up or the volume of the object as X times X times X equals X^3 or three dimensions, and this describes the space or volume.

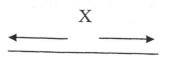

The line is X long.

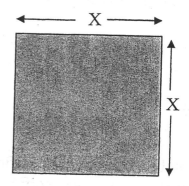

The area is X times X or X^2.

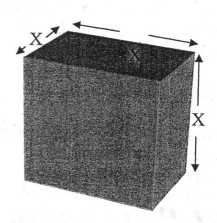

The volume is X times X times X or X^3.

Matter also possesses density. Density is the amount of matter found in a given volume.

Mathematically we can show this as:

$$D = \frac{M}{V} \quad \text{or} \quad DENSITY = \frac{MASS}{VOLUME}$$

Which weighs more, a pound of lead or a pound of feathers? This old question has tripped up a lot of people. Of course, a pound is the same weight whether in lead or feathers. What throws people off is that it is the density of lead and feathers that is different. A container of lead would weigh a great deal more than the same size container of feathers.

Another way of describing density is to use the term specific gravity. Specific gravity is the density of a substance compared to the density of water. Water that has a mass of one gram (gm), occupies the volume of one milliliter (ml).

$$\text{Density of water} = \frac{1 \text{ gm (mass)}}{1 \text{ ml (volume)}} = 1 \text{ }^{gm}/_{ml}$$

$$\text{Specific gravity of urine} = \frac{\text{Density of urine}}{\text{Density of water}} = 1.0014 \text{ ca.}$$

The specific gravity of water becomes the standard. Any substance with a specific gravity below one, when put in water will rise, and any substance with a specific gravity of greater than one will sink in a container of water. Just look at a bottle of Italian salad dressing. Why does the oil appear near the surface? The more material that is dissolved in water, the higher the specific gravity.

What is matter made up of? Take a piece of paper, which is composed of cellulose. Tear the paper into smaller and smaller pieces, till you can't see the pieces with the naked eye. Now using a magnifying glass, place these pieces under a microscope, which magnifies the pieces, so you can see them once again and continue tearing the paper into smaller pieces. Eventually we will arrive at the point where we divide the paper into pieces no longer retaining the physical and chemical properties of cellulose. The smallest particles, that still possesses those properties is called a molecule. If we go beyond this by dividing up a molecule, we would be left with atoms the smallest particles that make up elements. We can then say that matter is composed of atoms and molecules

The matter we are most familiar with exists in one of three possible states, solid, liquid or gas. The class into which a substance falls depends on physical conditions, such as the temperature and pressure that exists when it is observed. Under different conditions a single substance can exist in any one of the three states. Let us take water as an example. Water can exist as ice, a solid; water, a liquid or vapor, a gas, depending upon its temperature. Other substances such as iron and most other metals, which are not familiar to us in the liquid or gaseous states, can exist in these states if the temperature is high enough, for example molten iron is a liquid.

a. SOLIDS: Bodies that have a definite size or volume, and a definite shape.

b. LIQUIDS: Material that has a definite volume, but no definite shape. It takes the shape of the container it is put in.

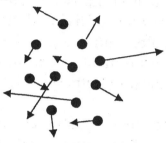

c. GASES: Substances which do not have a definite volume or a definite shape. Gas will fill any container.

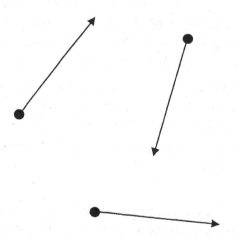

In all three states the molecules or atoms move. In a solid they seem to vibrate in place maintaining the overall shape of the object. In a liquid they are able to slide over one another, this allows us to pour a liquid. Finally in a gas, they move much more rapidly, being able to spread out in all directions to fill any container they are put in.

In general we can say that solids, liquids and gases differ as to the space between their particles, or to put it another way, how far apart their particles are. In a solid the particles are very close together, in a liquid the particles are farther apart and in a gas there is even more distance between the particles. Another way to express this is to say that gases, liquids and solids vary as to their density, that is the amount of mass per volume. The denser a substance is, the more mass per volume that it has. Solids are denser and therefore heavier than liquids, and liquids are denser than gases.

MEASUREMENT

Everything in the universe is composed of matter and possesses energy. Therefore to understand the fundamentals of living things, you need to understand some of the basic properties of matter and energy. To understand these properties we should consider their measurement. Measurement is also vital to the scientific process. The testing of most hypotheses relies on some form of measurement.

For measurement to have meaning, so it can be compared and communicated between people, it must be based on agreed-upon standards. The standard that you are probably most familiar with is the English system of standards. The system was built from a variety of arbitrary designations by the trades people. Their so-called standards would be different from person to person. Finally, to resolve the problem, by royal decree, the king of England, in the year 1100 declared that the distance from his nose to the thumb at the end of his outstretched arm was a yard. The inch started as a "rule of thumb". The width of his thumb. When the king stretched his hands out on both sides, that was all he could fathom, with that the standard was referred to as a fathom. He must have had a big foot, because that standard became the foot. These and all the other units of measurements were later more precisely standardized. Items with the precise measurements are stored at the bureau of standards in Washington D.C..

Today in our country each trade uses their own established standards, which are only widely used by people within those trades. The average person is usually not familiar with these measurements. For example if you were a woodsman, you would sell your firewood by the cord, or maybe a face cord. A jeweler would sell gold by the pennyweight, or troy ounce, which is different than an ounce of anything else, because a pound of gold weighs 12 ounces and not 16. If you were jockey in a horse race you would be familiar with furlongs, a pharmacist, with scruples, grains, and drams. A farmer, with a bushel and a peck. Sailors, with fathoms, knots, and leagues. Paper sellers, reams and quires, to name just a few.

Unfortunately some of the standards we use today go by the same name to add to the confusion. An ounce is one example. 16 ounces in a pint, 16 ounces in a pound of potatoes, and 12 ounces in pound of gold. All these ounces have different meanings. Our system of measurement is all too confusing and should be changed. We can do better than this in the technological age of the 21st century.

There are three basic types of measurement, length, volume, and mass. In 1793 the metric system was born in France. Based on a common substance, water, and using units to the base ten. In the metric system the basic unit can even be multiplied or divided by tens. When this is done, we add the appropriate prefix to the basic unit, as shown in the table below. Some of these prefixes are used more commonly than others. The ones with an asterisk (*) are the ones most commonly used.

Metric Prefixes for Modifying Basic Units					
Prefix	Abbr.	Multiple of the basic unit			Example
Tera...	T	One trillion times ...	10^{12}	1,000,000,000,000	Terabytes
Giga...	G	One billion times ...	10^9	1,000,000,000	Gigabytes
Mega...	M	One million times ...	10^6	1,000,000	Megabytes
Kilo...*	k	One thousand times ...	10^3	1,000	Kilograms
Hecto...	h	One hundred times ...	10^2	100	Hectometer
Deka...	da	Ten times ...	10^1	10	Dekagram
Basic unit	none	One times...	10^0	1	liter
Deci...	d	One tenth of ...	10^{-1}	0.1	Deciliter
Centi...*	c	One hundredth of ...	10^{-2}	0.01	Centimeter
Milli...*	m	One thousandth of ...	10^{-3}	0.001	Milligram
Micro...	μ	One millionth of ...	10^{-6}	0.000001	Micrometer
Nano...	n	One billionth of ...	10^{-9}	0.000000001	Nanometer
Pico...	p	One trillionth of ...	10^{-12}	0.000000000001	Picogram
* The more common prefixes					

The basic metric unit for length is the meter, which is equal to 39.37 inches, or a little bit longer than the yard. The most commonly used prefixes are the kilometer (km), a little greater than a half a mile. Smaller than the meter, we find the centimeter (cm), 2.54 cm equal 1 in., or to put another way a little less than half an inch. The smallest length used by the public commonly is the millimeter (mm), 25.4 mm equal 1 in..

If we leave length, and go over to mass, the basic unit in the metric system is the Gram (gm). 454 grams equal 1 pound, or 28.375 grams to the ounce. The most common prefixes with the Gram are the kilogram (kg), which is equal to 2.2

pounds. Smaller than the Gram, is the milligram (mg), which is the unit used for many common drugs to be measured.

We finally go to volume with a liter (l) the basic unit. The common units are the liter is equal to 1.06 quarts or the ml is equal to 1/1000 of a liter or about 20 drops depending on the liquid measured. Since water is the standard for the metric system, we can compare all of the standard units for length, mass, and volume. If we weigh one gram of pure water it has a volume of one ml and can be placed in a cubed container which measures in size, 1 cm by 1 cm by 1 cm or 1 cm cubed, a cubic centimeter, or cc, thus for water:

$$1cc = 1gm = 1ml$$

UNITS OF TEN

The metric system is based upon units of ten. Let's look at this a little closer. The number one is equal to 10^0, or ten to the zero power. The superscript zero is referred to as an exponent, as this exponent is raised, each time it is multiplied times ten, as follows:

$10^0 = 1$
$10^1 = 10$
$10^2 = 100 = 10 \times 10$
$10^3 = 1,000 = 10 \times 10 \times 10$
$104 = 10,000 = 10 \times 10 \times 10 \times 10$
$10^5 = 100,000 = 10 \times 10 \times 10 \times 10 \times 10$
$10^6 = 1,000,000 = 10 \times 10 \times 10 \times 10 \times 10 \times 10$

This is also true for numbers less than one. These fractions of one will have negative exponents.

$10^0 = 1$
$10^{-1} = 0.1 = 1/10$
$10^{-2} = 0.01 = 1/100$
$10^{-3} = 0.001 = 1/1,000$
$10^{-4} = 0.0001 = 1/10,000$
$10^{-5} = 0.00001 = 1/100,000$
$10^{-6} = 0.000001 = 1/1,000,000$

SCIENTIFIC NOTATION

Much of the calculations that are carried out in science deal with very large or very small numbers. These calculations are cumbersome to carry out, unless the numbers are put into scientific notation. Usually this is done by using a coefficient, a number between 1 and 10. It is by convention that we use one digit to the left of the decimal point when writing the coefficient. This is followed by the exponent of the power of ten.

Suppose we wanted to put the following number into scientific notation: 4,360,000. 10^6 equals 1,000,000, so the coefficient in this case would be 4.36. In its complete form 4.36×10^6. Another example, this time less than one. Put this number into scientific notation: 0.00024. The exponent in this example would be 10^{-4}, and the coefficient 2.4. This is written using scientific notation as 2.4×10^{-4}.

Complex calculations using scientific notation are simplified. When multiplying, using scientific notation, you add the exponents and multiply the coefficients. When dividing, using scientific notation, you subtract the exponents and divide the coefficients.

An example: How many 32's are there in 10,000,000? Begin by putting both numbers into scientific notation.
$32 = 3.2 \times 10^1$, and $10,000,000 = 1.0 \times 10^7$. For the coefficients you divide 1 by 3.2, or $1/3.2 = 0.3125$, and the exponents are subtracted $10^7 - 10^1 = 10^6$, therefore your answer is 0.3125×10^6 which is equal to 3.125×10^5 or 312,500.

Try to figure out the following problems using scientific notation:

1) How long does it take light to travel from the sun to the earth, if the distance between them is 93,000,000 miles, and light travels at 186,000 miles/second?

2) If a star is 13.7 light years away from earth, how many miles away is it? A light year is how many miles light travels in a year.

3) If a microorganism measures 1 picometer in length, how many organisms end to end would you find in 1 centimeter?

ENERGY

The classic definition of energy is the ability to do work. I guess now we have to define work. Work is the result of a force, a push or pull, moving an object a certain distance. How much force and how great a distance, describes the amount of energy. Which object is moved describes the form the energy takes. We can now try to simplify the definition of energy by eliminating the ability. You either have it or you don't, and if you don't, you don't have energy. So, now we are down to moving an object a certain distance. As we saw before, the object describes the form the energy takes, and its distance, the amount of energy. What we are left with is movement. So in its simplest form energy is movement.

There are two kinds of energy, kinetic or actual moving energy, carrying out work, and potential or energy at rest. Here the energy is stored waiting to be released. The ultimate source of all energy within our solar system is the sun.

CONSERVATION OF MATTER AND ENERGY

Matter and energy are not made or lost, however both can be changed into different forms. This statement describes what is known as the first law of thermodynamics (therm meaning heat and dyn meaning movement). If we look at the piece of paper we tore up to eventually get to the atom, remember it was made up of cellulose. We could burn the paper and as it burns a tremendous amount of heat energy would be liberated and we would see some smoke or small particles of the combustion or burning products going off. Invisible gases such as carbon dioxide and water vapor would be lost. We might be left with an ash that was blackened showing the element carbon. Some of the ash might be white or gray showing traces of other elements or minerals. When all these changes are done with, what has occurred is a redistribution of both the matter and as you will see the energy that was in the piece of paper. The paper in other words wasn't destroyed, it was simply changed into these other components.

In this second example suppose we had taken the same piece of paper and buried it in the backyard. What would happen to it then? After a period of time the paper would seem to disappear. What actually happens is it becomes food for countless microorganisms. As they feed on the paper similar reactions as found in the burning example occur, but in slower steps so the microorganisms can save the energy and use the energy to remain alive, just like you when you eat food.

The first law of thermodynamics calls for the transformation of the energy, and the second law describes order and disorder. This second law of thermodynamics is much more complex than the first and can be simply summarized as: all isolated systems that contain energy lose some of it as excess heat, thus lowering the efficiency of the system. All systems that are orderly in their composition will slowly go toward a disorderly composition over time. This disorder is called entropy. All natural processes tend to increase in entropy. An example of this can be a car which uses gasoline as potential chemical energy. The gasoline is combined with oxygen and exploded to release heat energy to move the car forward. However not all the energy is used efficiently. A lot of it escapes or is lost as heat energy. We know this because the engine gets hot, and the tires of the car will heat up as a result of the friction with the ground over which they rotate. In the winter some of this heat can be used to warm the inside of the car. The automobile engine is not very efficient in its use of gasoline.

An example using entropy might be found where you live. Everything is neatly arranged and will only remain that way as long as you expend energy to maintain it that way. If you don't, the system will increase in entropy, in other words, disorder and chaos. Living organisms stop this increase in entropy from occurring as long as energy is added to the organism from food.

THE FORMS OF ENERGY

We can describe seven forms that energy may take. Energy can be transformed from one form to another or others. . Let's become more familiar with each of them.

CHEMICAL ENERGY: chemicals are held together by chemical bonds. When these bonds are formed or broken, energy may be released. If we study the element sodium, we would note that it is a very reactive gray metal that must be stored under mineral oil to keep it from spontaneously reacting with the oxygen in the air. Chlorine the element is a very reactive yellow gas that is highly toxic and heavier than air. When a green pea size piece of sodium is dropped into a beaker containing chlorine gas, a powerful explosion would spontaneously occur resulting in a white smoke, when tasted it turns out to be common table salt or NaCl. This reaction released energy when the chemical bonds between the chlorine and the sodium were produced. The energy that was released when the bonds were formed in this example took the form of sound, because you can hear the explosion. Mechanical energy if it broke windows or moved objects, radiant and heat energy if the explosion was great enough to measure these characteristics. This reaction was shown before when we discussed symbols.

$$2Na + Cl_2 \longrightarrow 2NaCl + energy$$

Note that matter can't be made nor destroyed. Thus what is found on one side of this equation must be equal to what is found on the other side. The energy on the right side of the equation was also present on the left side as potential chemical energy. This process is called balancing an equation.

Now let's show this chemical energy is produced when chemical bonds are broken. Let's take the organic compound called methane. Methane is a gas that is used to cook with. Methane looks like this:

$$\begin{array}{c} H \\ | \\ H-C-H \\ | \\ H \end{array}$$

The lines represent the bonds in organic compounds.

$$\begin{array}{c} H \\ | \\ H-C-H \\ | \\ H \end{array} + 2O_2 \longrightarrow CO_2 + 2H_2O + energy$$

Note again that we balanced the equation. The energy we get by breaking the bonds of the methane is in the form of the heat we are cooking with, and radiant energy because we can see the flame.

CHEMICAL ENERGY IN LIVING ORGANISMS

Potential chemical energy in living organisms involves the phosphate polyatomic ion bonded to another compound. When the phosphate bond is broken, energy is released. The energy to reattach the phosphate is supplied by food the organism eats or makes. Green plants make their own food, while most animals eat their food. This food is broken down releasing the energy to attach the phosphate. The richest and most common form of potential chemical energy in living organisms is a compound known as adenosine triphosphate or abbreviated ATP.

When adenine, a nitrogen containing base, usually found in nucleic acids is combined with ribose, a sugar also found in nucleic acids, we produce adenosine.

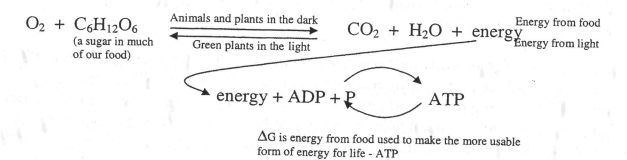

$O_2 + C_6H_{12}O_6$ (a sugar in much of our food) ⇌ [Animals and plants in the dark / Green plants in the light] $CO_2 + H_2O + energy$ [Energy from food / Energy from light]

energy + ADP + P ⇌ ATP

ΔG is energy from food used to make the more usable form of energy for life - ATP

If the adenosine is phosphorylized meaning we add a phosphate polyatomic ion, energy is needed to accomplish this. We now have adenosine mono (one) phosphate or AMP. If a second phosphate is added, much more energy is needed to accomplish this. Now we have formed adenosine di (two) phosphate, or ADP, this second phosphate is attached as a high-energy bond that is shown with the symbol ~ instead of the symbol --. If we repeat this step again we finally synthesize adenosine tri (three) phosphate which again requires much energy to attach the third phosphate which results in a second high energy bond. Much of the energy buildup takes place going from ADP to ATP, where in living organisms, food supplies the energy needed to a add on the third phosphate to make ATP. When the organism needs energy it simply converts the ATP back to ADP, and phosphate, to yield the energy that was stored in the high energy bond. Green plants are said to be autotrophic (auto means self, troph meaning energy), this means they make their own food. They do this through the process of photosynthesis where radiant energy from the sun is captured by a pigment called chlorophyll, and raw materials like water which is taken up through the roots and carbon dioxide which is taken in through the leaves are converted to sugar and oxygen. Plants only carry on photosynthesis while the sun shines. When there is no light they also rely on ATP that they produce from the food they made.

ELECTRICAL ENERGY: the things that move in this form of energy are electrons. To learn about electrons we must take a close look at the atom where they are found. The center of the atom is called the nucleus and contains the bulk of the mass. Two different subatomic particles can make up the nucleus, the proton and the neutron. Much further away from the nucleus we find our third type of particle, the electrons. All three particles differ in mass as well as in the electrical charge they possess. The proton acts as the standard for the mass of the atom, with one proton being equal to one atomic mass unit or AMU. The electron on the other hand has hardly any mass at all and when we compare it to the proton, it weighs in at only 1/1837 of an AMU. The neutron is really composed of the combination of the other two, and as such, the heavyweight, coming in at a mass of 1 and 1/1837 of an AMU..

Electrical charge is a difficult concept to describe. It is a force, a push or pull. We have all heard the sayings "opposites attract each other", and "likes repel each other". This is true of these electrical charges. The proton has a positive electrical charge and the electron a negative charge. When they are brought together they form a neutron, which results in a neutralizing of their respective charges, or a 0 charge.

Subatomic particle	Electrical charge	Atomic mass
Proton	+	1 AMU
Electron	-	$1/1837$
Neutron	0	$1\ 1/1837$

Of all three particles, it is the electron which is lightest and free to move the most. Therefore it is within these particles that we find the most energy. These electrons can be transferred from one object to another through friction. Much like when you rub a balloon against your clothes, it will stick to the wall, or your clothes in the dryer will stick to each other, "static cling". The more we rub the balloon, the more electrons are transferred. We are building up an electrical potential. A net difference in the number of electrons from one object to the other. The greater this disparity, the greater the electrical potential. The electrons remain where they are, they are static or stopped, until the potential becomes so great that they are able to jump from one object to the next. This describes static electricity. An example of this occurs when you walk on a carpet, when the air is dry and touch a light switch. The electrical potential builds up until it discharges to equalize the electrons and of course you get an electrical shock. You may even see a spark. On a grander scale the same thing happens with a lightning strike. In a big thunderhead cloud there are updrafts and downdrafts of air causing friction and a buildup of the electrical potential. When the electrons finally jump to the closest object they can discharge to, usually referred to as the ground, a lightning bolt is seen.

Another form of electricity is current electricity where electrons flow like the current in a river. The electrons flow through wires. To describe how this works, an electrical utility company using a generator causes an electrical potential to flow through wires, as long as the electrons can travel through a complete circuit. The thickness of the wire is just like the diameter of a garden hose determining the resistance to flow, if the pressure through the wire or hose remains the same. With electrical flow, increased resistance to flow, restated is friction, and friction becomes heat. This describes how the filament of a light bulb glows to give off light and heat.

In living things such as man, the flow of electrons is needed to react with both the external and internal environment. Specialized cells called sensory receptors transmit electrical impulses to the central nervous system where decisions are made to transmit other electrical impulses to an effecter, either a gland or a muscle, so that the proper response can be made.

6 **MECHANICAL ENERGY**: this type of energy is the most common one we see. Movement of an object is mechanical energy. A pair of scissors, a pen or pencil, an automobile, or any other object capable of movement is considered mechanical energy. In living organisms examples of the objects that move can be bones or muscles attached to fins in fish, wings in birds, or legs and arms in man.

2 **RADIANT ENERGY**: radiant energy is energy that radiates out from its source, when there is an acceleration of electrical charges. It seems to travel in waves or bundles of radiant energy called photons or quanta. All of this energy travels at the same speed, the speed of light, 186,000 miles per second. Let's look at a typical wave

If a stone is dropped into a body of water, the water will form a wave radiating out from its source, the dropped stone. The length of the wave is measured from one top or crest to the next, or from one bottom or trough to the next. This can also be considered one complete cycle of the wave. Before the wave was generated the water was at rest. That point or level we will call the resting point. From the resting point to the trough or crest is considered the height of the wave or amplitude. As the wave travels the number of cycles of the wave that pass a given point in a second is called its frequency or cycles per second. Since with radiant energy all these waves travel at the same speed, there is an inverse relationship between frequency and wavelength. The longer wavelengths must give rise to lower frequencies and vice versa. High frequency waves pack much more energy in them and because their wavelengths are shorter can pass between atoms and molecules more readily.

ANATOMY OF A WAVE

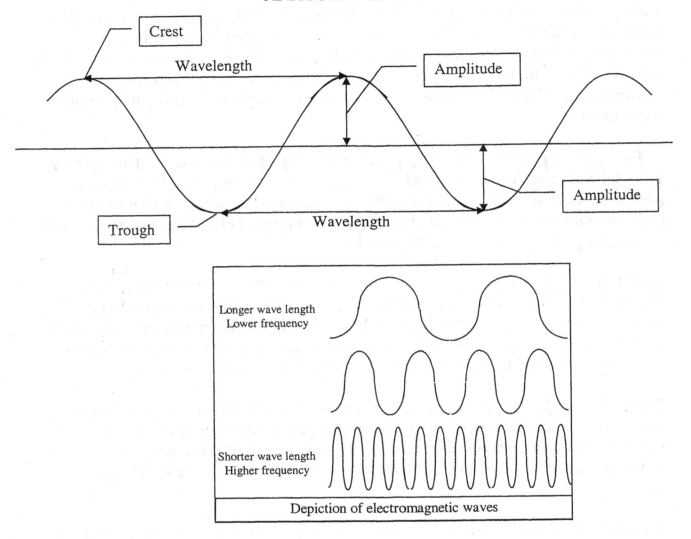

Depiction of electromagnetic waves

Carefully examine the radiant waves more closely we find they have electrical as well as magnetic properties. Because of this wall radiant energy makes up what we call the electromagnetic spectrum, beginning with a harness frequencies shortest wavelength and ending with the lowest frequency and longest wavelengths.

When radioactive materials decay, they emit gamma radiation, which is able to pass through most objects, because of its high frequency or energy state and extremely short wavelength. X-rays are able to do the same. By using a film sensitive to x-rays we allow them to pass through our bodies to expose x-ray film

Electromagnetic Spectrum

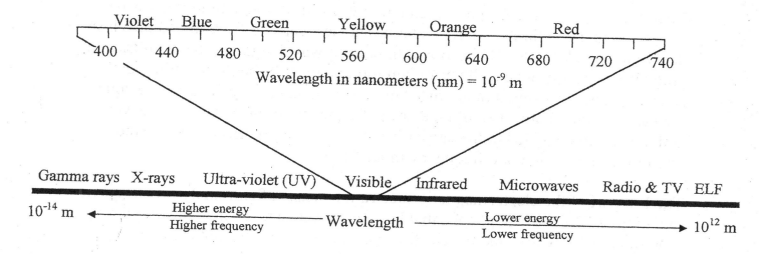

when we take a chest x-ray or have the dentist x-ray your teeth. The lead apron he puts on you protects your sex cells from any radiation damage that might occur. Both gamma radiation and x-rays are ionizing radiation. Because when they pass through material they form ions or charged particles from atoms.

Ultraviolet or black light is considered non ionizing radiation, but it excites molecules. It is called black light because it is not visible to our eyes. Ultraviolet means beyond violet, so that visible light begins with violet, goes through all the colors of the rainbow and winds up with red. The visible spectrum of light is made up of all these colors and when combined produces white light. When this light shines on an object, for example, that is blue, all the light is absorbed except blue which is reflected to our eyes and registers blue in our brain. If an object is black, the light is all absorbed and nothing is reflected to our eyes therefore black is the absence of color. When the object is white no light is absorbed. All of it is reflected to our eyes and we see white.

Infrared is a form of heat energy, which is radiating from its source and warms things. Scopes that can see this radiation, and show these warm objects are used as sniper scopes, or to make heat seeking missiles. Infrared pictures could be taken using film sensitive to infrared thus separating the hot from cold areas, when doing an energy audit of your home or taking satellite pictures of ocean currents or farmland. Infrared heat lamps keep your hamburger warm in the fast food restaurants. Radar is used to produce radiation that travels great distances and if it strikes objects is reflected back to the source. Distance, size, and speed of the object can be calculated.

Microwaves are used for communication, TV transmission, and in microwave ovens where they vibrate mainly water molecules, causing friction and thus heat to defrost and cook foods. Radio waves have long wavelengths, capable of traveling great distances and are excellent for communications. When a specific radio station is tuned in using a radio, the station is assigned a specific carrier frequency. By varying (modulating) amplitude or the frequency, information such as voice and music can be added to the carrier wave. Thus we get AM and FM radio, amplitude modulation and frequency modulation.

The last part of the electromagnetic spectrum consists of extremely low frequency radiation or ELF. Any appliance that has electromagnetic energy flowing through it produces ELF. Clock radios, electric shavers, power lines, and the like.. Little is none of the health effects of such radiation at present.

Examples of the role of radiation in living organisms is the process of photosynthesis, where plants use the green pigment chlorophyll to absorb certain frequencies of visible light energy, to be able to produce carbohydrate and oxygen, using carbon dioxide and water. In animals the complex organ that acts as a receiver of visible light is the eye. What the eye sees is interpreted by the central nervous system as images that we recognized as our visible world.

HEAT: in this form of energy molecules and atoms move. This heat is transferred from substance to substance three different ways conduction, convection, and radiation. If you use the thermometer to measure the temperature of a substance, you are measuring the degree of heat or the speed of the molecules or atoms temperature can be measured using three different scales. Fahrenheit is the system we use in the United States. Celsius is the system used by the rest of the world, and the entire scientific community. Kelvin is used by scientists involved in the study of very low temperatures. Absolute zero is the temperature at which matter ceases to move. Scientists have never achieved absolute zero.

Important Temperatures			
	Fahrenheit	Celsius	Kelvin
Boiling point of water	212 °F	100 °C	373 °K
Human body temperature	98.6 °F	37 °C	
Room temperature	68 °F	28 °C	
Freezing point of water	32 °F	0 °C	273 °K
Absolute zero	-459 °F	-273 °C	0 °K

To measure the amount of heat, the calorie is the unit often used. The calorie is the amount of heat energy required to raise the temperature of 1 gram of water 1 degrees Celsius. It is the large calorie or kilocalorie, 1000 times greater than the calorie, which is used in nutrition. Very often if greater amounts of heat are described, as in appliances like air-conditioners, water heaters, a different unit is used. The British thermal unit or BTU, is described as the amount of heat energy required to raise the temperature of a pound of water one degree Fahrenheit.

Conduction is when heat is transferred molecule to molecule, like the handle of a pot on a stove heating up over time. Convection is when heat is transmitted by liquid or gas, as it heats up it expands, becomes less dense and rises, while the more dense material falls to take its place. Radiation is transferring heat via the electromagnetic radiation of infrared energy. An example is the warmth of a heat lamp, or the direct heat from a fireplace. An example of heat is the warmth of warm blooded organisms such as man. This is the result of entropy of the system, which is expressed as heat. The temperature of 98.6 degrees Fahrenheit, is necessary for sufficient speed of reactions (metabolism) to maintain all the bodies functions, such as muscle action, which is the result of the breakdown of ATP.

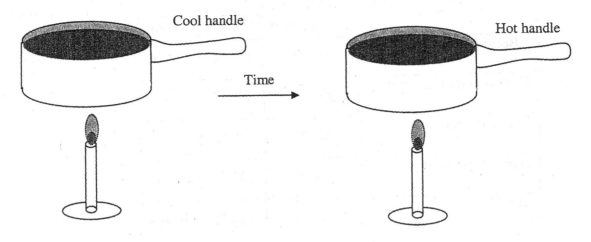

Cool handle

Time

Hot handle

Conduction

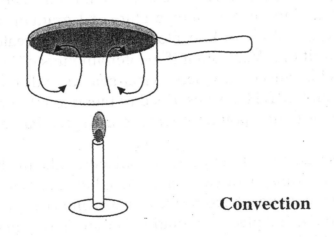

Convection

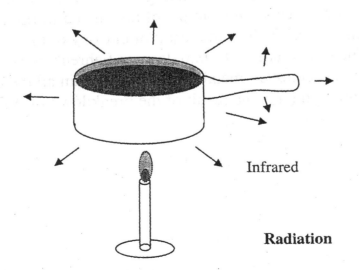

Infrared

Radiation

$\curvearrowright$ <u>SOUND</u>: in this form of energy the objects that move, vibrate, producing sound waves which are received by our ears and interpreted by the central nervous system. Examples are sonar which is used to determine the depth in the oceans, the plucking of a string on a banjo, or the vibrating vocal cords when you speak.

Since sound produces waves, frequency or cycles per second, or vibrations per second can be described as pitch, how much bass or treble the sound produces. Loudness is determined by the amplitude, the amount of energy, and the distance from the sound source. This sound pressure or intensity is measured using the unit called the decibel (db). Each increase of 10 db, is equal to a tenfold increase in sound intensity

Levels of sound		
Example	Description	Decibels
Hearing threshold	Just below audible	0
Ticking wrist watch	Just audible	10
Talking	Normal speech	60
Vacuum cleaner	Loud	80
Dance club	Hearing loss likely	100

<u>NUCLEAR:</u> or atomic energy is the energy contained in the nucleus of the atom. There are two distinctly different ways that this energy can be released. The first is nuclear fission (splitting) where a very large atom such as uranium is struck by a fast-moving neutron. The nucleus of the atom is split apart into two fragments, which release some more neutrons that go on to hit other uranium atoms, causing the chain reaction releasing a great amount of heat. If uncontrolled, an explosion, or thermo nuclear device, an atomic bomb goes off. When under control this heat can be harnessed in a nuclear reactor to produce usable electrical energy.

The second type of nuclear energy is fusion. In fusion two hydrogen nuclei are fused together to form a helium atom nucleus and a tremendous amount of energy. To initiate the reaction a great deal of heat energy must be liberated, the equivalent of an atomic bomb detonation. This is the reaction that occurs continuously on the sun and is responsible for all the life on our planet. The thermonuclear bomb that can be created using this fusion reaction is called a hydrogen bomb. As yet there is no way to harness peacefully the fusion reaction, unless it could be started at low temperatures. The search for the so-called "cold fusion" has not been productive as yet.

Fission Chain Reaction

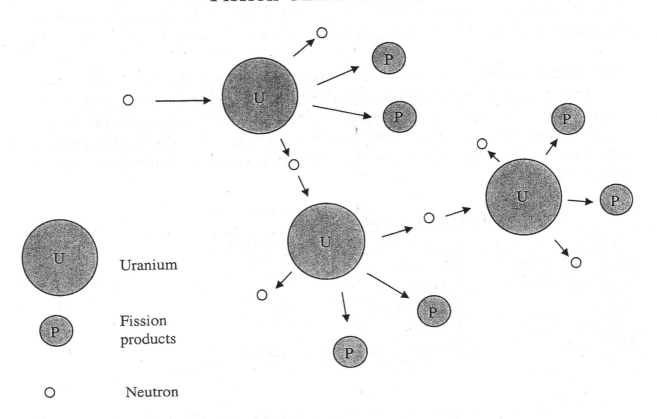

U   Uranium

P   Fission products

O   Neutron

Fusion

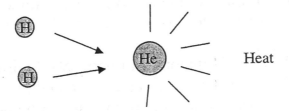

Heat

INTRODUCTION TO INORGANIC CHEMISTRY

Chemistry deals with the composition of matter. All matter can be subdivided into three divisions. These are elements, compounds, and mixtures.

If a substance is not capable of being broken down into simpler substances using ordinary means, then that substance is elementary in our universe, or said to be an element.

If we look at air, we find it is made up of different gases mixed together. If sugar is mixed with water, we get a mixture. The water can be allowed to evaporate and the sugar will crystallize to its original form. A mixture therefore is material where different types of matter are mixed together, but each type retains its original characteristics. If the type of matter can be decomposed to yield simpler substances using ordinary means, then it is considered a compound.

The history of modern chemistry can be traced back to the Egyptian civilization. Unfortunately much of what they learned was lost. In the Middle Ages, the great science thinker's searched for a way to convert base metals to precious ones, like gold. They were known as the alchemists. This word is derived from an ancient tongue where "chem" means "Egypt" and "al" is Arabic for "from". The literal translation therefore refers to "from Egypt". Since most of known science had its roots in the earlier Greek and Roman periods, the elements were known by their Latin names. The chemical symbols used today for many of the elements, come from the Latin.

Examples of Latin Symbols

Element	Latin Name	Symbol
sodium	natrium	Na
potassium	kalium	K
iron	ferrum	Fe
lead	plumbum	Pb
copper	cuprum	Cu
gold	aurium	Au
silver	argentum	Ag
mercury	hydragyrum	Hg

Most elements use as their symbol the letter or first two letters they begin with. The first letter is always capitalized and the second letter is in lowercase. Examples of substances that exist as elements around us might be a diamond in a ring, or the graphite in a pencil, these are pure forms of the element carbon. We may find a piece of aluminum, or iron, or the individual gases found in the air.

The elements are organized in a chart called the periodic table of the elements. There are ninety-two naturally occurring elements, and additional man-made ones that we will not discuss. We are most interested in those elements found in living organisms. The main ones are carbon, hydrogen, oxygen, and nitrogen. Phosphorus, calcium, sodium, potassium, sulfur, and others play a lesser role.

The following is the periodic table of the elements. An asterisk is shown with the most important of these elements.

Periodic Table of the Elements

Metals — Transition Elements — Nonmetals

Legend: Atomic Number → Symbol (H), Element Name (Hydrogen), Atomic Weight (1.0079) — Mass

1	2	3	4	5	6	7	8	9	10	11	12	13	14	15	16	17	18
1 * H Hydrogen 1.0079																	2 * He Helium 4.003
3 Li Lithium 6.941	4 Be Beryllium 9.012											5 B Boron 10.811	6 * C Carbon 12.011	7 * N Nitrogen 14.007	8 * O Oxygen 15.999	9 F Fluorine 18.998	10 Ne Neon 20.180
11 * Na Sodium 22.990	12 * Mg Magnesium 24.305											13 * Al Aluminum 26.982	14 Si Silicon 28.086	15 * P Phosphorus 30.974	16 * S Sulfur 32.066	17 * Cl Chlorine 35.453	18 Ar Argon 39.948
19 * K Potassium 39.098	20 * Ca Calcium 40.08	21 Sc Scandium 44.956	22 Ti Titanium 47.88	23 V Vanadium 50.942	24 Cr Chromium 51.996	25 Mn Manganese 54.938	26 * Fe Iron 55.847	27 Co Cobalt 58.933	28 Ni Nickel 58.69	29 * Cu Copper 63.546	30 Zn Zinc 65.39	31 Ga Gallium 69.723	32 Ge Germanium 72.61	33 As Arsenic 74.922	34 Se Selenium 78.96	35 Br Bromine 79.904	36 Kr Krypton 83.80
37 Rb Rubidium 85.47	38 Sr Strontium 87.62	39 Y Yttrium 88.906	40 Zr Zirconium 91.224	41 Nb Niobium 92.906	42 Mo Molybdenum 95.94	43 Tc Technetium (98)	44 Ru Ruthenium 101.07	45 Rh Rhodium 102.91	46 Pd Palladium 106.42	47 * Ag Silver 107.87	48 Cd Cadmium 112.41	49 In Indium 114.82	50 Sn Tin 118.71	51 Sb Antimony 121.75	52 Te Tellurium 127.60	53 I Iodine 126.90	54 Xe Xenon 131.29
55 Cs Cesium 132.90	56 Ba Barium 137.33	◆ 57–71 Lanthanide series (rare earth elements)	72 Hf Hafnium 178.49	73 Ta Tantalum 180.95	74 W Tungsten 183.85	75 Re Rhenium 186.21	76 Os Osmium 190.2	77 Ir Iridium 192.22	78 Pt Platinum 195.08	79 * Au Gold 196.97	80 Hg Mercury 200.59	81 Tl Thallium 204.38	82 * Pb Lead 207.2	83 Bi Bismuth 208.98	84 Po Polonium (209)	85 At Astatine (210)	86 Rn Radon (222)
87 Fr Francium (223)	88 Ra Radium (226)	◊ 89–103 Actinide series (radioactive earth elements)	104 Unq Unnilquadium (261)	105 Unp Unnilpentium (262)	106 Unh Unnilhexium (263)	107 Uns Unnilseptium (262)	108 Uno Unniloctium (265)	109 Une Unnilennium (266)									

41

The Atom

The smallest unit of an element is the atom. Let's review what we already know about the atom as previously covered, and add to that information. The center of the atom is called the nucleus and is made up of a cluster of two kinds of subatomic particles, protons and neutrons. Outside the nucleus we find the third type of subatomic particle, the electron. They seem to form a cloud because of their light mass and great speed. The number of electrons outside of the nucleus is always equal to the number of protons inside the nucleus in an atom, so that the total electrical charge of the atom is zero.

Electrons are found moving in specific orbital patterns and according to different models these patterns are propeller-like or spherical. We find these electrons in concentric shells, levels, or orbits around the nucleus, and as we go further away from the nucleus the electrons are freer to move, thus the electrons in the outermost shell are the most important in allowing atoms to combine. They are referred to as the valence electrons. Two electrons fill the innermost energy level, and in the small atoms that we are most concerned about, the following levels and the outer energy levels each have a top capacity of eight electrons. If we look at the periodic chart of the elements, each column number corresponds to the number of valence electrons. All the elements of the first column have one valence electron, the second column two valence Electrons, the third through the twelfth column, one or two valence Electrons, the next zigzag columns, three, four, five, six, and seven, until we get to the last column, where each element is complete with eight, except the first element which as we stated earlier is complete with only two.

The protons of the nucleus have a mass equal to 1 AMU, and a positive electrical charge. The number of protons in each atom also serves to identify the element you are working with; this is referred to as the atomic number. One just counts the number of protons in the atom. As an example, if there are eight protons in an atom, the atomic number is eight and the element whose atomic number is eight, is oxygen. This is seen on the periodic table of the elements.

The neutrons of the atom are really just the combination of electrons with negative charges and protons with positive charges, these two electrical charges neutralize each other, and thus the neutrons have neutral electrical charges. The mass of the neutron is just slightly greater than that of a proton because of this slight mass of the electron, which is usually treated as zero. If you wanted to know the total mass of an atom, you would simply add together the number of protons, each with a mass of 1 AMU, and the number of neutrons, each with a mass of one AMU. This total is referred to as the mass number.

If we look at the periodic table of the elements, at phosphorus, symbol P, we see that it has the atomic number 15 and the mass number 31. That tells us that there are 15 protons, and of course, to balance these protons electrically we also find 15 electrons. We find two in the first shell, eight in the second, and five in the third, to add up to a total of 15. Next, since there are 15 protons in this atom, and it has a mass number of 31, the difference between these two numbers is reflected in the number of neutrons present. In this case it has to be 16.

ISOTOPES

An isotope is a different form of the same element. Isotopes have different mass numbers, but the same atomic number. If we look at isotopes closer, we see, that what makes them different, is the number of neutrons, which also makes them heavier. Some of these isotopes have the property of being radioactive, this means we find instability within the nucleus of the atom, and they emit high energy, subatomic particles as radiation. These isotopes are less commonly found than the stable atoms.

Isotopes of Hydrogen		
^1_1H Hydrogen	^2_1H Deuterium	^3_1H Tritium

IONS

An ion is a charged particle. Atoms are always electrically neutral. The particles of the atom that are usually free to be lost or gained are the valence electrons of the outermost shell. If the electron or electrons were lost, the atom would now become an ion with an overall positive charge. If an electron or electrons were gained, the atom would now become an ion with an overall negative charge. The most stable elements are those whose valence electron shell is complete.

THE PERIODIC TABLE

The elements found in the periodic table can be classified into four different groups based on their chemical reactivity. Metals, which have specific physical metallic properties. Most have one, two, or three valence electrons, which means that they are able to give up these electrons when they chemically combine, thus the next shell in becomes the outer shell. Nonmetals are the elements that have four to eight valence electrons. Those elements with four to seven valence electrons accept electrons from metallic elements when they combine, to fill their outer shell, and become stable. The inert elements sometimes called the noble gases are found at the extreme right side of the table. Their outer shell is complete and thus they are stable, inert, or non-reactive. The transitional elements are found between the true metals and nonmetals. Even though they are classified as metals, their chemical properties place them between the two.

If you read the periodic table like a book, you would see that the atomic number increases as you go from left to right and continues as you go down the table. The same is generally true for the atomic mass, which is not rounded off to account for the isotopic forms of the elements found in nature. From the information shown in the periodic table, you should be able to draw a representative atomic model for each of the elements. Let's examine one of these in detail, then, you can practice on your own. If we look at the element sodium, in the periodic table it appears as follows:

```
┌─────────────┐
│ 11          │
│    Na       │
│  SODIUM     │
│  22.990     │
└─────────────┘
```

Sodium is not found as an element naturally on earth because this metal is very highly reactive. It would immediately combine with other compounds or elements, like water, chlorine, or oxygen, and is thus found in the form of molecules of compounds. That is why pure sodium has to be stored in a bottle under mineral oil, to keep it from spontaneously reacting with other materials. The first thing we notice about the sodium atom is the atomic number 11. This tells us there are 11 protons with positive charges, and 11 electrons with negative charges to counterbalance the protons. The first shell would be filled with two electrons, the second with eight, and the third with only one, for a total of 11 electrons. Now we look at the atomic mass number, in this case 22.990. We can round the number off to the nearest whole number, 23. Since the mass of the atom is basically equal to the number of protons and neutrons in the nucleus, our chore is to calculate the number of neutrons. The atomic mass is 23 for sodium, if we subtract the number of protons from 23, we get 12, that is equal to the number of neutrons. We can now draw our atomic model.

Now practice drawing the atomic model of some other important elements asterisked in the periodic table.

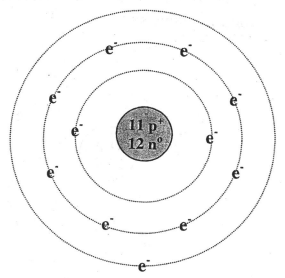

If the sodium atom shown above were to change to a more stable form, it could become an ion. To do this, the sodium atom would have to make its outermost shell complete, like the inert elements of the last column of the periodic table. The sodium atom would give up the electron in its outermost shell, because less energy is expended losing one electron than gaining seven electrons to make the outer shell complete. If we examine the ion, we now count 11 protons, 12 neutrons, but only 10 electrons. This ion has eleven positive charges, and 10 negative charges. That will give us a plus 1 charge for the sodium ion. The sodium ion is written as Na^+. Ions are usually formed as a result of the combining the two or more atoms that can satisfy one another by filling their outer shells, through the give-and-take of those valence electrons.

IONIC BONDING

If we look for an element that would be a good match for the sodium atom we just drew, chlorine comes to mind. Let's look at it in the periodic table:

| 17 |
| Cl |
| CHLORINE |
| 35.453 |

Chlorine is not naturally found on earth as an element because of how reactive it is. If we produce chlorine in the laboratory, it takes the form of a poisonous yellow gas. Chlorine has seventeen protons, seventeen electrons, and 18 neutrons. It has two electrons in the first shell, eight in the next, and seven valence electrons. Can you see why chlorine is a great match for the sodium atom? The sodium gives up its one valence electron to the chlorine, which takes it in to its last shell, thus completing it. Now both atoms are in a more stable form, as a compound, NaCl or common table salt.

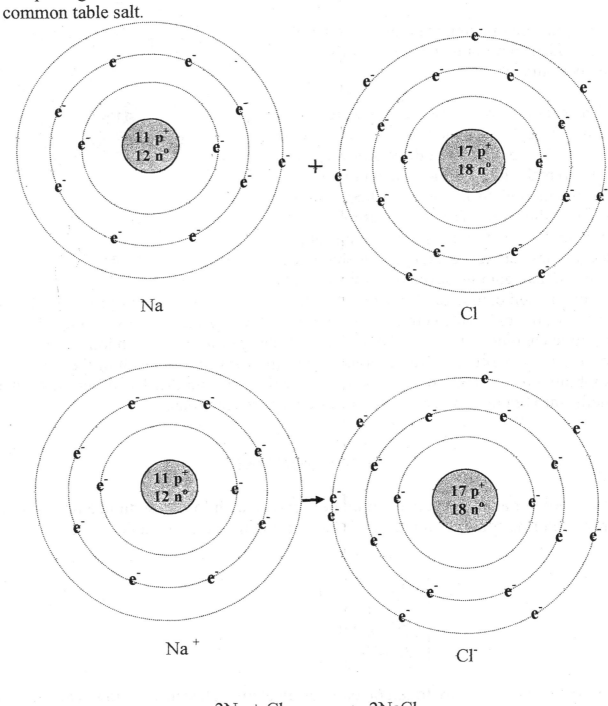

$$2Na + Cl_2 \longrightarrow 2NaCl$$

POLYATOMIC IONS

Some ions contain more than one element these are referred to as polyatomic ions. OH^- is the polyatomic ion called hydroxide. The O has a valence of -2, and the H has a valence of +1. Together they have in net valence of -1. This OH is treated as a single unit, which can be combined with other ions to form a molecule of a compound. A few examples follow:

NH_4^+ = ammonium, CO_3^{-2} = carbonate, SO_4^{-2} = sulfate, and PO_4^{-3} = phosphate. As an example NH_4^+ can combine with OH^- to form NH_4OH ammonium hydroxide. The valence of some of these polyatomic ions are determined by several characteristics that are beyond what you have to know at this point.

TYPES OF INORGANIC COMPOUNDS

There are four types of inorganic compounds. These are acids, bases, salts, and oxides. We will learn about each of them.

ACIDS: These are compounds which are able to give up, or donate hydrogen ions or H^+ in solutions, because of this, inorganic acids normally begin with the symbol for hydrogen. Most acids are toxic or caustic. If you could taste acids, they would have a sour taste like citric acid in lemons, or vinegar, which is acetic acid. The following is a list of some common inorganic gases and their formulas.

HCl = HYDROCHLORIC ACID = Found in your stomach.
H_2SO_4 = SULFURIC ACID = Found in car batteries.
H_2CO_3 = CARBONIC ACID = Found in Seltzer or club soda.
H_3PO_4 = PHOSPHORIC ACID = Found in some soft drinks.

BASES: these are inorganic compounds that give up or donate the hydroxide ion or OH^- when in solutions. The formula for bases always ends with OH^-, and usually begins with a metallic element. Most bases are toxic or caustic. If you could taste a base, it would have a bitter taste. Cocoa is treated with lye (sodium hydroxide) to give it a bitter taste. The following is a list of some common inorganic bases and their formulas.

NH_4OH = AMMONIUM HYDROXIDE = Household ammonia.
$NaOH$ = SODIUM HYDROXIDE = Lye, found in drain and oven cleaners.

KOH = POTASSIUM HYDROXIDE = Found in hair removers.
$Ca(OH)_2$ = CALCIUM HYDROXIDE = Lime.

pH

pH is a simple way to express how acidic or basic a solution is, or more simply the concentration of hydrogen ions in this solution. It is defined as the negative exponent of the hydrogen ion concentration. Pure water, H_2O, or HOH, contains just as much hydrogen ion as hydroxide ion. In one liter of water, the hydrogen ions weigh 0.0000001 grams, or 1×10^{-7} grams. Lets use the definition of pH. Since the hydrogen ions in one liter of water weighs 1×10^{-7} grams, the negative exponent of 10^{-7} is 7, so the pH of water is 7. Therefore the lower the pH the more hydrogen ion and the higher the pH the less hydrogen ion. Pure base would have a pH of 14, while pure acid would be at 0.

THE pH SCALE

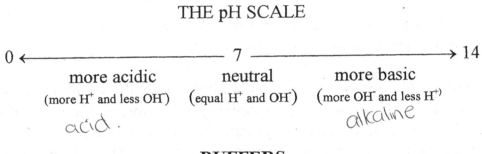

0 ←———————	7	———————→ 14
more acidic	neutral	more basic
(more H^+ and less OH^-)	(equal H^+ and OH^-)	(more OH^- and less H^+)
acid .		alkaline

BUFFERS

A buffer is a chemical substance, which is able to maintain or resist changes in the pH of a solution, by either absorbing hydrogen ions or hydroxide ions. Living organisms are extremely complex systems and must be able to balance all internal environmental factors to survive. PH is one of these factors. The pH of the blood ranges from 7.35 to 7.45. If it goes below 7.35 the person goes into a condition known as acidosis and will die if not corrected. A pH above 7.45 will lead to alkalosis and the person will die if not treated. To prevent these conditions natural buffers are found in all living organisms.

SALTS: The third type of inorganic compound can be formed by reacting acids with bases. This type of reaction is called neutralization. These neutralization reactions always yield a salt and water. As an example let's take lye, NaOH, very caustic. If you to feel a weak solution of sodium hydroxide, it would feel slippery. That is because it is dissolving your skin! Now let's look at HCL, hydrochloric acid. This could dissolve foods in your stomach, and if a drop or two would be pushed up and out of the stomach, you would suffer from heartburn, which is literally burning the tissue of your esophagus or gullet. When these two powerful chemical opposites are combined we simply get salty water.

$$NaOH + HCl \longrightarrow NaCl + H_2O$$
sodium hydroxide + hydrochloric acid $\longrightarrow$ sodium chloride + water

Let's now look at other salts that could be formed, by simply combining the acids previously listed with the bases previously listed.

$HCl + NaOH \longrightarrow NaCl$ = sodium chloride + H_2O
$HCl + NH_4OH \longrightarrow NH_4Cl$ = ammonium chloride + H_2O
$HCl + KOH \longrightarrow KCl$ = potassium chloride + H_2O
$HCl + Ca(OH)_2 \longrightarrow CaCl_2$ = calcium chloride + H_2O

Practice producing salts by using the other acids and bases listed.

OXIDES: The fourth group of inorganic compounds are the oxides. These are simply an element combining chemically with oxygen, examples are:

CO_2 = Carbon dioxide, produced during combustion of carbon containing fuels.
CO = Carbon monoxide, produced if insufficient oxygen is provided for during combustion.
SO_2 = Sulfur dioxide, produced when burning fuels containing elemental sulfur.
FeO = Iron oxide, a brown compound commonly called Rust.
CuO = Copper oxide, a green compound, like the covering of the Statue of Liberty.

CHEMICAL REACTIONS

Chemical reactions occur when two or more substances react to produce new substances. There are three main types of reactions.

1) Direct combination or synthesis reactions - the building up or making more complex substances from simpler ones.

$$A + B \longrightarrow AB$$

2) Decomposition or analytic reactions - the breaking down of complex substances to simpler ones.

$$AB \longrightarrow A + B$$

3) Exchange or substitution reactions - the reactants switch partners or change places.

$$AB + CD \longrightarrow AD + BC$$

If energy is needed for a reaction to occur it is referred to as endergonic or endothermic. If energy is released during a chemical reaction it is referred to as exergonic or exothermic. Most reactions can be reversible, meaning the arrows above can go in the opposite direction based on the amount of substance or energy available.

ORGANIC CHEMISTRY

You go to supermarket to buy food. All the food you see is natural, meaning it is not artificial. It's derived from living organisms. The word organic means pertaining to living substances. Both of these words are "healthy living" buzzwords. If produce is grown in the absence of artificial substances, such as chemical fertilizers, pesticides (insect killers), and herbicides (weed killers), it is said to be organically produced. It stands to reason therefore that inorganic chemistry should pertain to substances not derived from living organisms, and organic chemistry should pertain to substances derived from living organisms. Such was the case before the year 1828 when the German chemist named Wohler, was able to take an inorganic chemical, and by heating it produced an organic chemical, which previously was thought to only come from living organisms.

$$NH_4NCO \xrightarrow{\text{heat}} NH_2-\overset{\overset{\displaystyle O}{\|}}{C}-NH_2$$

AMMONIUM CYANATE   UREA (found in urine)
(inorganic)   (organic)

Organic chemistry is no longer easily separated from inorganic chemistry simply by how a compound is formed. Today we consider the study of organic chemistry to involve compounds containing the element carbon. Carbon is a unique element. Life on our planet is based on this element.

$$^{12}_{6}C$$

Let's examine its atomic structure. With an atomic number of 6 it has six protons and six electrons. With an atomic mass of 12, it also has six neutrons.

With four valence electrons, a carbon atom is not very reactive ionically. Carbon instead is able to share pairs of electrons with other atoms, including other carbon atoms. This sharing of pairs of electrons is called covalent bonding and is important to the study of organic chemistry.

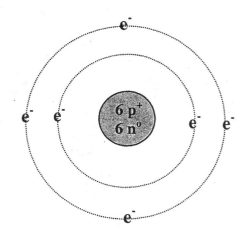

COVALENT BONDING

The element hydrogen is a gas, that is normally found as H_2, or as two atoms bound together.

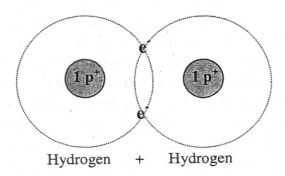

Hydrogen   +   Hydrogen

Each of the above hydrogen atoms, seem to share the other's electrons, thus filling their outer electron shells. H_2 is a more stable form of hydrogen. Through this covalent bonding we can form other so-called diatomic molecules as well. Cl_2, N_2, and O_2 to name a few.

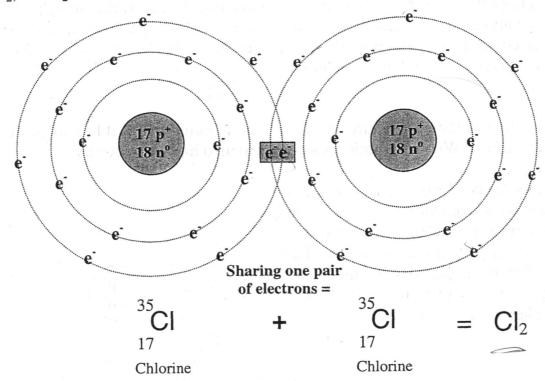

Sharing one pair
of electrons =

$^{35}_{17}Cl$ + $^{35}_{17}Cl$ = Cl_2

Chlorine   Chlorine

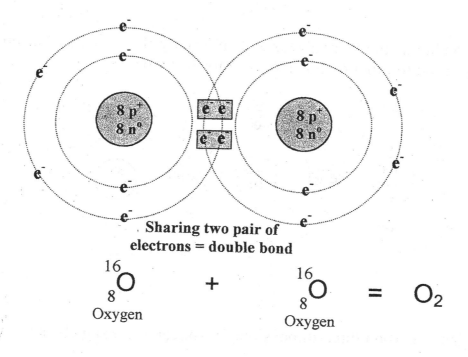

Sharing two pair of electrons = double bond

$^{16}_{8}O$ Oxygen   + $^{16}_{8}O$ Oxygen   = O_2

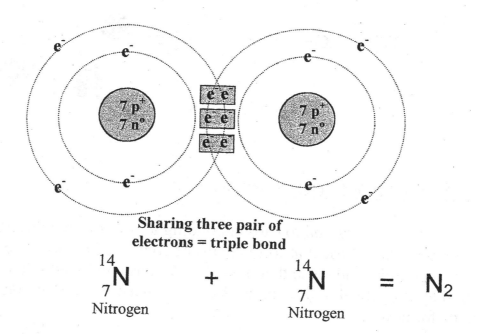

Sharing three pair of electrons = triple bond

$^{14}_{7}N$ Nitrogen   + $^{14}_{7}N$ Nitrogen   = N_2

Carbon atoms when they bond produce a structure that is three-dimensional, with bond angles of 109 degrees from each other.

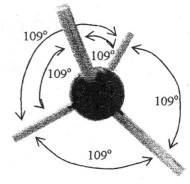

When carbon bonds to other substances it normally shares pairs of electrons. Carbon can bond to other carbon atoms to form chains.

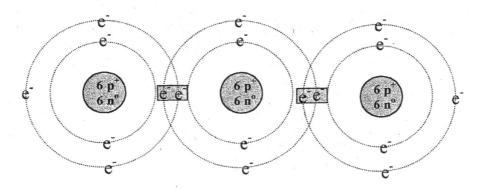

These chains of carbon three-dimensionally appear as zigzag chains.

ALIPHATIC VS. AROMATIC COMPOUNDS

The uniqueness of this carbon to carbon bonding allows for two different types of organic compounds. Those that form chains of connected carbons are called aliphatic compounds, and those that have the carbons combined into a closed ring are referred to as cyclical or aromatic. We will concentrate mainly on the aliphatic compounds for now.

Aliphatic

cyclical

HYDROCARBONS

The simplest aliphatic organic compounds contain just two elements hydrogen and carbon. These compounds are called hydrocarbons. There are thousands of possible hydrocarbon compounds that exist, but we will only learn about some of them, to be able to grasp an understanding of the basics of organic chemistry.

The simplest family of hydrocarbons are the alkanes. Alkanes are naturally derived from petroleum. These organic compounds all end in "ane". The first one is methane, which looks like this.

$$H \overset{\overset{\displaystyle H}{\bullet}}{\underset{\underset{\displaystyle H}{\bullet}}{\bullet\bullet C \bullet}} H$$

Notice that four pairs of electrons are shared with the carbon which allows each hydrogen its two electrons to fill its outer shell and the carbon with four pairs or eight electrons to fill its outer shell. Instead of these dots we will use a line to represent each pair of electrons.

$$\begin{array}{c} H \\ | \\ H-C-H \\ | \\ H \end{array} \quad \text{methane}$$

We can write a formula for methane as CH4, but this doesn't represent the molecule as well, because it does'nt show it's actual bonds. Methane is the lightest and smallest of the alkanes. It is found as a gas together with the next larger alkane, which is ethane. Together the two are used as natural gas, to heat your house, dry your clothes, heat your water, or cook your food. Natural gas is highly combustible and explosive.

$$\begin{array}{cc} H & H \\ | & | \\ H-C-C-H \\ | & | \\ H & H \end{array} \quad \text{ethane}$$

The third alkane also a gas at room temperature is combustible and can be put into cylinders under pressure till the molecules are so compressed that they become a liquid. This gas is the one used in outdoor barbecues. This alkane is called propane or LP gas, LP standing for liquid petroleum.

$$H-\underset{\underset{H}{|}}{\overset{\overset{H}{|}}{C}}-\underset{\underset{H}{|}}{\overset{\overset{H}{|}}{C}}-\underset{\underset{H}{|}}{\overset{\overset{H}{|}}{C}}-H \qquad \text{propane}$$

The fourth member is less combustible and less explosive. It is liquefied using much less pressure. Put into a clear plastic container, it is sold as a "Bic" lighter. This gas is butane.

$$H-\underset{\underset{H}{|}}{\overset{\overset{H}{|}}{C}}-\underset{\underset{H}{|}}{\overset{\overset{H}{|}}{C}}-\underset{\underset{H}{|}}{\overset{\overset{H}{|}}{C}}-\underset{\underset{H}{|}}{\overset{\overset{H}{|}}{C}}-H \qquad \text{butane}$$

Notice, however as the molecules become larger, the physical properties change. Hydrocarbons with from 5 -12 carbons are considered gasoline. Now we have gone from the gaseous state to the liquid state at room temperature. However, this liquid mixture of hydrocarbons is very volatile. When it burns in an automobile it is too explosive. An 8 carbon form of octane burns less explosively and smoother. The more of this octane, the less pinging in the engine, and the more expensive the gasoline.

A more viscous liquid is formed from hydrocarbons going from 12 to 15 carbons. This less combustible liquid is called kerosene. As we going to larger sized hydrocarbons we go from diesel fuel to more viscous lubricating motor oils for automobiles, to Grease, and petroleum jelly "Vasoline", to paraffin waxes and finally Asphalt. That is as solid as solid as one can find

ALKENES AND ALKYNES

Alkenes are hydrocarbons having at least one double bond, and alkynes are those with at least one triple bond. Let's look at these double and triple bonds.

$$\overset{}{\underset{}{>}}C\ \ C\overset{}{\underset{}{<}} \qquad \text{or} \qquad \overset{}{\underset{}{>}}C=C\overset{}{\underset{}{<}}$$

carbon-to-carbon double bond

If carbon to carbon bonds are formed with the sharing of two pairs of electrons, then that second pair is harder to form and therefore it is easier to break. This we will call a double bond. Simple hydrocarbons containing these double bonds, all end in "ene". An example of an alkene is ethene.

$$\underset{H}{\overset{H}{\diagdown}}C=C\underset{H}{\overset{H}{\diagup}} \qquad \text{ethene}$$

If three pairs of electrons are bonded together, this is called the triple bond. This triple bond is even easier to break, releasing more energy when it breaks. The first alkyne containing at least one triple bond is ethyne, or by its common name acetylene, the gas used to produce a very high burning temperature in an oxy-acetylene torch.

$$-C{\equiv}C- \qquad \text{or} \qquad H-C{\equiv}C-H \qquad \text{acetylene}$$

Carbon-to-carbon triple bond

SUBSTITUTED HYDROCARBONS

a group of other hydrocarbons are formed when hydrogens are replaced with other components, such as chlorine. These are referred to as substituted hydrocarbons. Some examples of these compounds follow:

$$\underset{H}{\overset{H}{\underset{|}{\overset{|}{H-C-H}}}} \qquad \text{Replace a H with a Cl} \rightarrow \qquad \underset{H}{\overset{H}{\underset{|}{\overset{|}{H-C-Cl}}}}$$

Methane   Methyl chloride

Replacing two more H's and we get this: $\quad \underset{Cl}{\overset{Cl}{\underset{|}{\overset{|}{H-C-Cl}}}}$

and finally this:

$$
\begin{array}{c}
\text{Cl} \\
| \\
\text{Cl}-\text{C}-\text{Cl} \\
| \\
\text{Cl}
\end{array}
$$

All three of these compounds can be toxic to the lungs, liver, and kidneys, and therefore are not used as much in household products anymore.

remove hydrogen

ORGANIC RADICALS

Any hydrocarbon compound which lacks a hydrogen, is incomplete, but can be treated as a single unit, which can combine with other units to form a complete compound. This incomplete unit is referred to as an organic radical. These radicals all end in "yl". The first four organic radicals follow:

Complete

Alkanes	Alkane radicals
H | H–C–H | H methane	H | H–C– | H methyl
H H | | H–C–C–H | | H H ethane	H H | | H–C–C– | | H H ethyl
H H H | | | H–C–C–C–H | | | H H H propane	H H H | | | H–C–C–C– | | | H H H propyl
H H H H | | | | H–C–C–C–C–H | | | | H H H H butane	H H H H | | | | H–C–C–C–C– | | | | H H H H butyl

FUNCTIONAL GROUPS

These and other radicals can combine with atoms or groups of atoms which are responsible for the chemical properties of the completed organic compound. These groups are called functional groups. Each family of organic compounds has its specific functional group. Let's look at some of these families.

ALCOHOLS

The first family of important organic compounds containing a functional group, that we will look at, is the alcohols. The functional group that all alcohols contain is OH, the hydroxyl group. To be an alcohol, we simply combine any organic radical with the functional group OH.. The general formula for all alcohols is simply R-OH, where the R stands for the organic radical. If we use the first three organic radicals we previously discussed, we would get the following alcohols.

Alcohols can end in "ol".

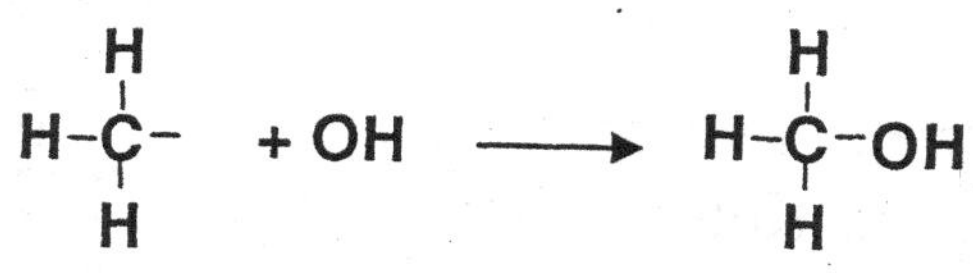

H–C– + OH $\longrightarrow$ H–C–OH

Methanol

Methanol's common name is wood alcohol, because it is derived by heating wood in the absence of air. It is used as a thinner for shellac, or for dry gas which is added to automobile gas tanks in winter to prevent gas line freezing. If ingested methanol can cause blindness or death.

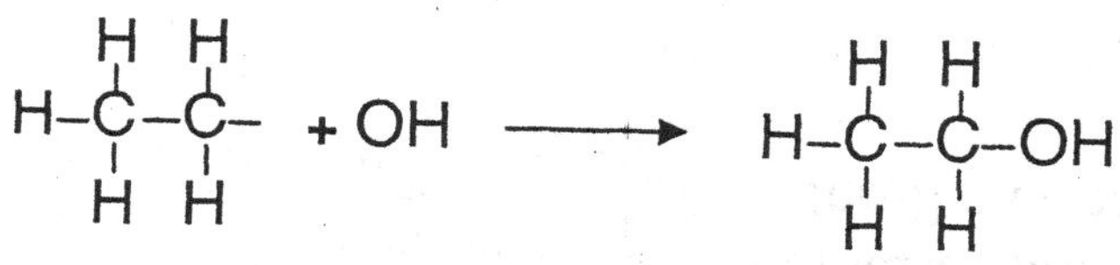

H–C–C– + OH $\longrightarrow$ H–C–C–OH

Ethanol

Ethyl alcohol or ethanol, has as its common name grain alcohol, because it is derived from fermenting grains and other complex carbohydrates to make alcoholic beverages.

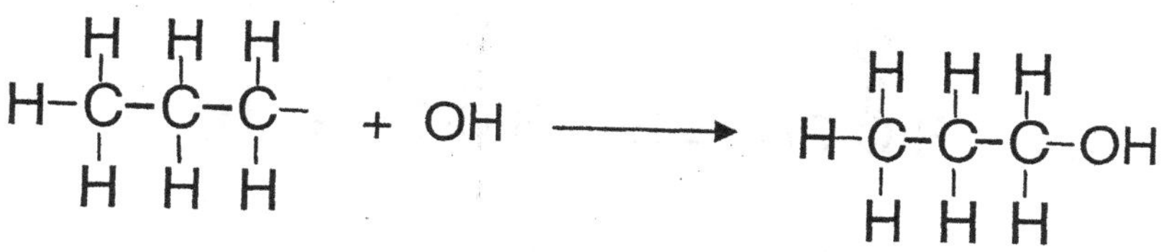

H–C–C–C– + OH $\longrightarrow$ H–C–C–C–OH

Propanol

Propyl alcohol or propanol, is a form of rubbing alcohol sold in pharmacies, called isopropanol.

ALDEHYDES AND KETONES

Both of these families share the same functional group, C=O, the carbonyl group. If the functional group is at the end of the organic radical it is considered an aldehyde with the general formula shown.

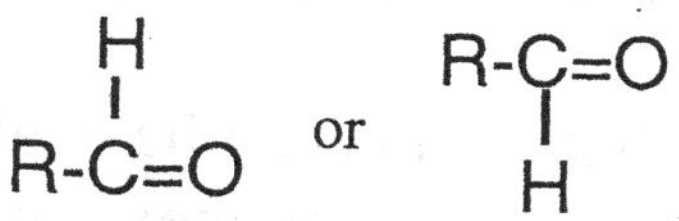

H
|
R–C=O   or   R–C=O
|
H

General formula of aldehydes

The smallest and most important aldehyde is the gas

formaldehyde, which when dissolved in water makes formalin, used in embalming fluid, a preservative.

$$H-\overset{\displaystyle H}{\underset{}{C}}=O$$

Formaldehyde

If the carbonyl functional group is found between two organic radicals, then the family represented is a ketone. Ketones have the general formula shown.

$$R-\overset{\displaystyle O}{\overset{\|}{C}}-R$$

Ketones

The smallest ketone is dimethyl ketone or acetone. This is used as a solvent for laquers or nail polish.

$$H-\overset{\displaystyle H}{\underset{\displaystyle H}{C}}-\overset{\displaystyle O}{\overset{\|}{C}}-\overset{\displaystyle H}{\underset{\displaystyle H}{C}}-H$$

Acetone

CARBOXYLIC ACIDS

This family has as its functional group, $\overset{\displaystyle O}{\overset{\|}{C}}-OH$ called the carboxylic group. The general formula for these acids is as shown.

$$R-\overset{\displaystyle O}{\overset{\|}{C}}-OH$$

General formula for carboxylic acids.

Since fats are partially made from them, these acids are sometimes referred to as fatty acids. When dissolved in water they will weakly ionize to give H^+, as follows:

$$R-\overset{\displaystyle O}{\overset{\|}{C}}-OH \rightleftharpoons R-\overset{\displaystyle O}{\overset{\|}{C}}-O^- + H^+$$

These acids play an important role as food preservatives. The simplest carboxylic acid is formic acid.

$$H-\overset{\displaystyle O}{\overset{\|}{C}}-OH$$

Formic acid

Formic acid is the irritating acid injected via a bee, wasp, and Ant stings. The second carboxylic acid is acetic acid or in a diluted form, commonly called vinegar.

$$CH_3-\overset{\displaystyle O}{\overset{\|}{C}}-OH$$

Acetic acid

Propionic acid, the third one, is used as a preservative for breads.

$$CH_3CH_2-\overset{\displaystyle O}{\overset{\|}{C}}-OH$$

Propionic acid

These acids can have all single bonds between their carbons, in which case, they are said to be completely saturated, with all the carbons completely filled with hydrogens.

If the acid has one double bond between carbons, it is considered a monoun-saturated fatty acid.

$$H-\underset{\underset{H}{|}}{\overset{\overset{H}{|}}{C}}-\underset{\underset{H}{|}}{\overset{\overset{H}{|}}{C}}-\underset{\underset{H}{|}}{\overset{\overset{H}{|}}{C}}-\underset{\underset{H}{|}}{\overset{\overset{H}{|}}{C}}-\underset{\underset{H}{|}}{\overset{\overset{H}{|}}{C}}-\overset{O}{\overset{||}{C}}-OH$$

Saturated

$$H-\underset{\underset{H}{|}}{\overset{\overset{H}{|}}{C}}-\underset{\underset{H}{|}}{\overset{\overset{H}{|}}{C}}-\underset{\underset{H}{|}}{\overset{\overset{H}{|}}{C}}-C=\underset{\underset{H}{|}}{\overset{\overset{H}{|}}{C}}-\overset{O}{\overset{||}{C}}-OH$$

Monounsaturated

If this double bond were to break in the presence of hydrogen, it would become completely saturated once again. If a carboxylic acid has more than one double bond between carbons, it is considered a polyunsaturated fatty acid. We will talk more about these acids when we consider fats.

$$H-\underset{\underset{H}{|}}{\overset{\overset{H}{|}}{C}}-C=\underset{\underset{H}{|}}{\overset{\overset{H}{|}}{C}}-C=\underset{\underset{H}{|}}{\overset{\overset{H}{|}}{C}}-C=\underset{\underset{H}{|}}{\overset{\overset{H}{|}}{C}}-\overset{O}{\overset{||}{C}}-OH$$

Polyunsaturated

ESTERS

Esters are a family of organic compounds that are formed by reacting an alcohol with a carboxylic acid.

$$R-\overset{O}{\overset{||}{C}}-O\textcircled{H} + \textcircled{HO}-R \longrightarrow R-\overset{O}{\overset{||}{C}}-O-R + H_2O$$

ester bond

Fruits get their characteristic flavor and aroma from Esters. The fragrance of flowers is derived from esters. Perfumes are made from natural or synthesized Esters. Amyl acetate is banana oil, it tastes and smells like banana. Octyl acetate has the flavor of oranges, and ethyl butyrate smells like pineapple.

If one looks at a young bottle of wine, it has its tartness as a result of the presence of carboxylic acids. It also has its inherent alcohol. If allowed to age, each these two families organically react over time, to produce Esters. This mellows the wine removing the tart acids and producing a bouquet and aroma characteristic of various fruits.

AMINES

The last family we will discuss is the amines. The functional group found in the amines is the amino group NH_2. The general formula for amines is as shown. We will discuss the amino group when we talked about amino acids, the building blocks of proteins.

R-N-H
|
H

Amines

IMPORTANT FAMILIES OF ORGANIC COMPOUNDS

Organic families	Functional group	Name	Form
Alcohol	**OH**	hydroxyl	**R-OH**
Aldehyde	**C=O**	carbonyl	H | R-C=O
Ketone	**C=O**	carbonyl	O ‖ R-C-R
Carboxylic acid	O ‖ C-OH	carboxyl	O ‖ R-C-OH
Ester	O ‖ C-O-R	ester	O ‖ R-C-O-R
Amine	N-H | H	amino	R-N-H | H

These families are considered important to us, because each of these play a role in forming the biological molecules of living things, that we will next study in biochemistry.

BIOCHEMISTRY

The organic compounds we just learned about, play a vital role in the formation of the very large molecules that compose living things. These large molecules of life are referred to as **macromolecules**. The macromolecules can be divided into four main groups. The carbohydrates, proteins, lipids, and nucleic acids. With the exception of the lipids, the macromolecules are composed of many small organic building blocks that are joined together. When any chemical substance is made up of the same basic units repeated over and over again, this type of compound is referred to as a polymer. The basic unit is a monomer, two units bonded together produce a dimer, three a trimer, and so on.

CARBOHYDRATES

Carbohydrates are as the name describes, hydrates or waters of carbon. The general formula for carbohydrates is $(CH_2O)_n$, where n stands for a number. If n=6, then we would have $C_6H_{12}O_6$. All carbohydrates act chemically as polyhydroxyl aldehydes or ketones.

MONOSACCHARIDES

The simplest carbohydrates, the building blocks of the carbohydrate macromolecules are known as sugars or saccharides (sweet units). These compounds end in "ose", like maltose and glucose. The sugars are classified according to the number of carbons they possess, and whether they are aldehydes or ketones. Examples are aldohexoses, ketopentoses, or aldotrioses. The first one is a six carbon sugar with an aldehyde group. The second is a five carbon sugar with a ketone group, and the last is a three carbon sugar with an aldehyde group. Sugars can be found in two structural forms, either as an aliphatic (chain) structure, or more commonly as a ring structure.

The most common and most important of the sugars is glucose. A mono saccharide composed of one sweet unit. It is also known as dextrose, or grape sugar.

Notice that the carbonyl bond of the open form of glucose, opens up to form the ring structure by bonding to the next to the last carbon of the chain, which transferred its hydroxyl group to the first carbon.

Glucose

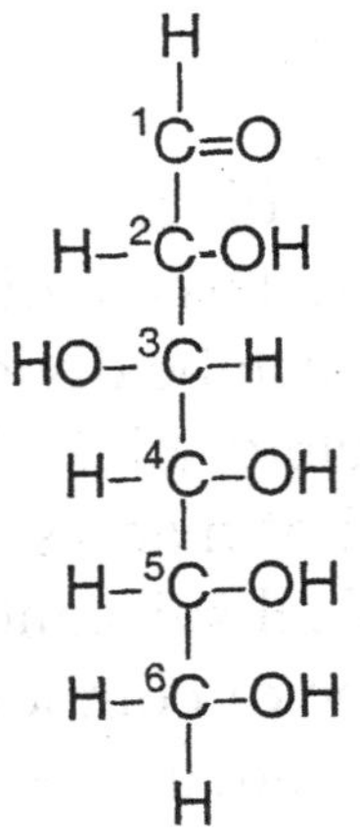

Chain form

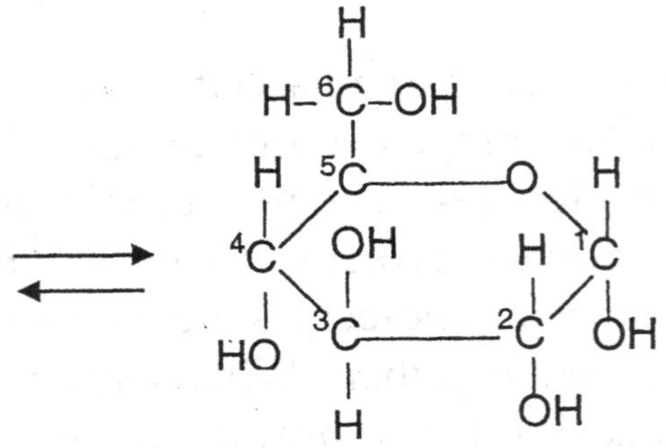

Ring form

Each carbon is numbered so you can follow
the changes in form

In plants, glucose is produced during photosynthesis. It allows the plant to produce energy for survival. Animals can take in foods containing glucose, which, when digested and transported to cells undergoes a series of reactions known as cellular respiration, which liberates energy for their survival. Most other sugars can easily be converted to glucose, making it most common.

Two other important hexoses are galactose, the monosaccharide found in milk sugar, and fructose, the sweetest of all sugars, associated with fruits. Notice that it is a ketohexose.

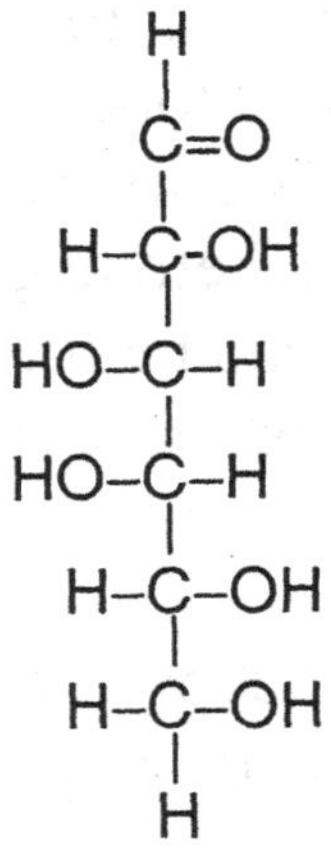

Galactose

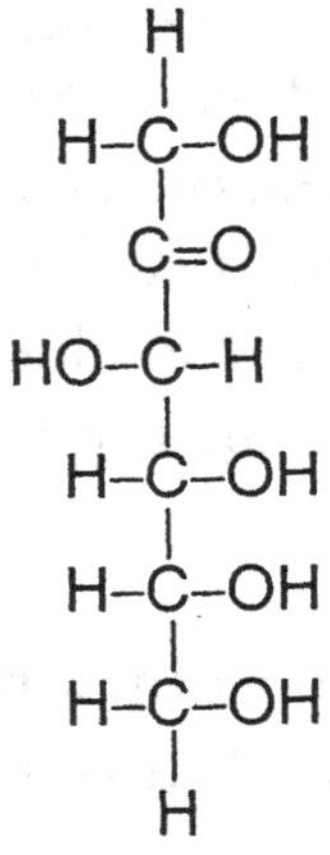

Fructose

Two other important monosaccharides are aldopentoses, or five carbon sugars containing an aldehyde function group, these are ribose and deoxyribose, found in nucleic acids and the ATP molecule.

Ribose – chain and ring form   **Deoxyribose** – chain and ring form

The difference between them is simply the removal of the oxygen from the second carbon of ribose to make it <u>deoxyribose</u>.

DISACCHARIDES

Through a reaction called dehydration synthesis, meaning to produce, by removal of water, two monosaccharides can be bonded together. The bond that links the two sugars together, is the glycosidic bond. Since the sugars occur mainly as ring structures, that is how they will be shown.

$\longrightarrow$ Dehydration synthesis
$\longleftarrow$ Hydrolysis

As you can see this dehydration synthesis reaction is reversible. The breakdown of disaccharide is referred to as a hydrolysis reaction, where water is added to aid in lysis or destruction of the Glycosidic bond.

$$\text{GLUCOSE + GLUCOSE} \rightleftharpoons \text{MALTOSE + H}_2\text{O}$$

There are three important disaccharides. Maltose, the one above, is most commonly derived from the grain, barley. It is the sugar found in malt liquors, malted milk balls, and malteds.

A second disaccharide is lactose or milk sugar, the slightly sweet sugar found in milk.

$$GLUCOSE + GALACTOSE \rightleftharpoons LACTOSE + H_2O$$

The third disaccharide is sucrose. You know this one as cane, beet, or common table sugar. This is the one you use as a sweetner for most things. It is sweet because it contains fructose.

$$GLUCOSE + FRUCTOSE \rightleftharpoons SUCROSE + H_2O$$

To manufacture very sweet syrups and candies, corn syrups and sucrose can be hydrolyzed to release the much sweeter fructose.

POLYSACCHARIDES

Poly means many. Monosaccharides are connected to one another through Glyco sidic bonds. This can be simplified as follows:

Monosaccharide   Disaccharide   Polysaccharide, as in starch or glycogen
(monomer)   (dimer)   (polymer)

Plants produce their own food in the form of monosaccharides, mainly glucose. The food that isn't immediately used for energy production is stored by the plant in an insoluble form, as starch. Cornstarch, rice, potato, and wheat starch, are a common food source for humans, as well. Most of the starch, the plant produces helps to form its offspring, as reserve food in its seeds. Corn kernels, for example are the seed for growing corn. When planted, the starch present is needed by the embryo for energy to germinate, and grow in the soil, until the young corn plant is able to spread its leaves, and carry out photosynthesis on its own. Natural starch is found as a mixture of two types of molecules,. A long straight chain and a long branched chain of Polyglucose.

Animals are able to store excess glucose in the form of a Polysaccharide found in muscles and the liver, called glycogen meaning to make sweet. When glucose is called for, the glycogen molecule is hydrolyzed. This Polyglucose molecule is more highly branched, than the starch molecules found in plants.

Also produced as a result of photosynthesis by the plant is cellulose. This very highly branched Polyglucose molecule has cross linkages which make its molecule look like Window screening. Cellulose makes up the very fiber of plants, their cell walls. Wood, cork, paper, and cotton are made of cellulose. The human body cannot digest this molecule, but cows can to some extent. Cellulose makes up the bulk of their diet.

Cellulose
Note how the bonds between the glucose units differ from starch or glycogen

LIPIDS

Lipids are a varied group of substances that are chemically different from one another, however, they all share one physical characteristic. Lipids are all insoluble in water.

Major Classes of Lipids
1) Fats and oils
2) Steroids
3) Fat soluble vitamins
4) Phospholipids

FATS AND OILS

The lipids found in greatest abundance are the fats and oils. The fats are usually associated with animals, and are generally solid at room temperatures. Bacon grease, lard, and butter, are examples of animal fats. The oils are usually associated with

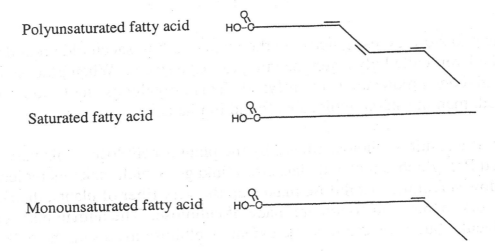

Polyunsaturated fatty acid

Saturated fatty acid

Monounsaturated fatty acid

plants, and are generally liquid at room temperatures. Olive, canola, Corn, and peanut oil are examples of the vegetable oils. Whatever the source of these fats and oils, they are all mixtures of different molecules. For example, you can taste huge variances in different olive oils and butter, because of their different molecular makeup. In animals, fats serve as a long term energy storage component, A typical fat, per gram, will yield more than twice as many calories as a gram of carbohydrate or protein. These fats, found in adipose tissue are also able to protect sensitive body structures from shock and provide insulation for the body. Fat people are often warmer than skinny ones.

To synthesize fat, the backbone, glycerol, or glycerin is used. It is a polyhydroxyl alcohol found in cosmetics and used as a base in cough syrups.

$$
\begin{array}{c}
H \\
| \\
H-C-OH \\
| \\
H-C-OH \\
| \\
H-C-OH \\
| \\
H
\end{array}
$$

Glycerol, a liquid polyhdyroxyl alcohol found in cosmetics and used as a base in cough syrups.

Also making up the fat molecule are three carboxylic acids (fatty acids), usually having an even number of carbons in each. As we described earlier there are two types of fatty acids those with all single bonds between the carbons, said to be saturated. Those that contain double bonds between the carbons are unsaturated – monounsaturated, if only one exists, and polyunsaturated if they contain more than one double bond. These double bonds cause the fat molecule to kink where they are found. As a result polyunsaturated fat molecules do not cozy up to one another as saturated fat molecules do. Saturated fats tend to form insoluble globs of fat in the arteries carrying blood. Blood's solvent is water, and lipids don't dissolve in water. These globs can eventually clog up your arteries, causing the hardening of the arteries or arteriosclerosis.

To synthesize a fat, the glycerol molecule combines with the three fatty acid molecules by forming an ester bond (esterfication). Water is removed in this synthesis, and like carbohydrates, we again have dehydration synthesis, and if the reaction is reversed, hydrolysis.

$R*$ = Organic radicals. These fatty acids can be the same, or different, depending on the source of oil or fat.

STEROIDS

Steroids are a group of lipids that contain a four ring aromatic structure.

Ring structure common to all steroids

The most common steroid contains an OH group and therefore ends in ol, cholesterol. Cholesterol is a component of cell membranes, and is the precursor of for the synthesis of other steroids. These include sex hormones, adrenocortical hormones, bile salts, and vitamin D.

Cholesterol

Testosterone

Cholesterol has been given a bad rap because it is not soluble in the blood, and can build up on the linings of the blood vessels narrowing the vessels diameter, and restricting blood flow. This plaque that forms also roughens the vessel walls and makes it easy for clots to form, cutting off blood flow, and triggering either a heart attack or stroke, depending upon where the clot forms. If the clot forms in the heart blood vessels, a heart attack. In the brain, a stroke. What is a person to do? Eat right, and exercise. Fill up on vegetables, fruits, fiber, and fish. Avoid high fat intake especially saturated fats.

FAT SOLUBLE VITAMINS

All vitamins are either water or fat-soluble. Those that are fat-soluble are classified as lipids, and include vitamin A, E, and K. Vitamin A is for vision in dim light, E as an antioxidant, and K to help clot your blood.

PHOSPHOLIPIDS

Phospholipids are lipids that are esterfied with a phosphate group, and play an important role, together with cholesterol, in forming cell membranes in all living cells, thus helping regulate what passes in and out of cells.

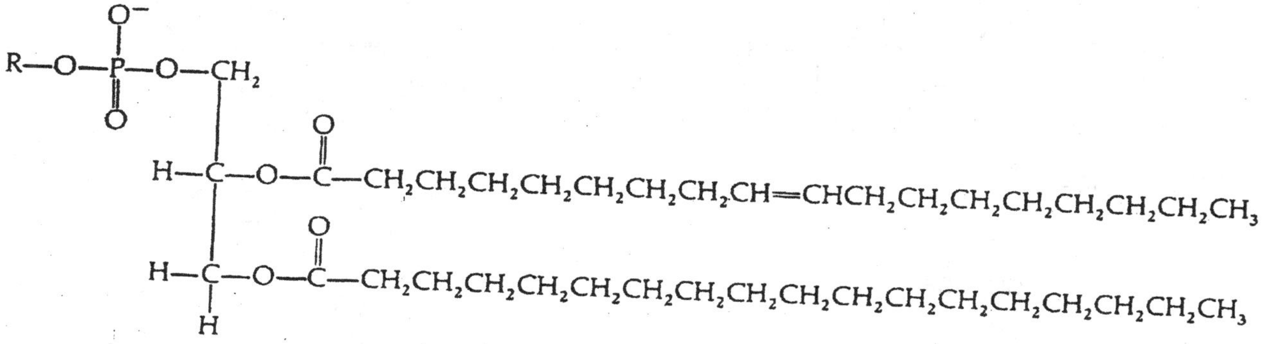

Phospholipid

Porphyrins

These are complex colored lipid-like molecules, all with a similar basic ring structure as shown:

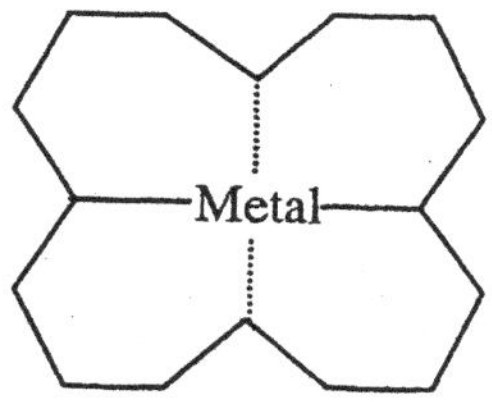

Porphyrin ring

The metallic component in the center of the ring structure determines which porphyrin we are dealing with. If the metal is iron, the porphyrin could be the heme molecule. This molecule is red in color, and when combined with a globular protein forms hemoglobin, the red oxygen carrying pigment of the blood.

The heme group in hemoglobin

A molecule of chlorophyll

Another example of the porphyrins is one with magnesium found in the center. This molecule is the green pigment found in plants, called chlorophyll. Chlorophyll is responsible for absorbing the suns energy to carry out photosynthesis.

Other porphyrins are the colored molecules of cells called cytochromes. These molecules are involved in energy transfer. These cytochromes contain iron or copper in their center. Vitamin B12 is a blue porphyrin containing the metal cobalt.

PROTEIN

The word protein is derived from prot meaning first or foremost. Of all the macromolecules, proteins are the most important and can be the most complex chemically. As much as half of your body's weight is protein. These molecules carry out more jobs in living things than any other type of macromolecule.

The basic building block of all proteins are amino acids. There are twenty naturally occurring amino acids, they differ from one another based on the radical (R).

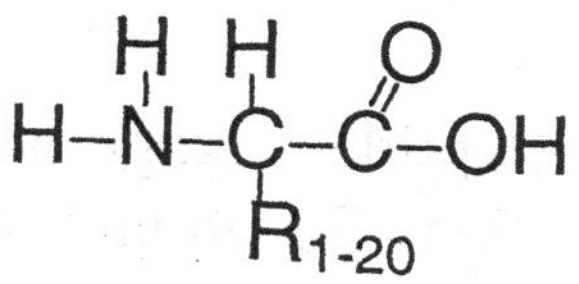

$$H-N-C-C-OH$$

with H, H, O above and R_{1-20} below

This radical is important in determining the physical, chemical, and ultimately the functional properties of the protein. The NH_2 (amino) group and COOH (carboxyl) group are both important in synthesizing chains of amino acids, called polypeptides. This is accomplished once again through dehydration synthesis. In this reaction two or more amino acids are bound together by the removal of water molecules, forming a strong bond referred to as the peptide linkage.

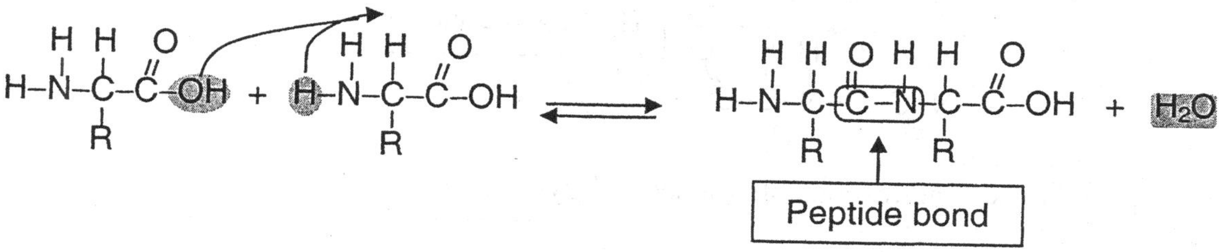

$$H-N-C-C-OH + H-N-C-C-OH \rightleftharpoons H-N-C-C-N-C-C-OH + H_2O$$

Peptide bond

Because there are twenty amino acids, the variation in their sequence can be enormous, leading to more varied protein molecules than any other macromolecule known. Proteins can be much more complex than simply polypeptides. Their structure can be subdivided into four degrees of complexity.

$1°$ or primary structure
$2°$ or secondary structure
$3°$ or tertiary structure
$4°$ or quaternary structure

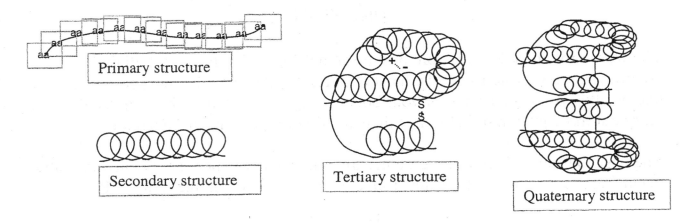

Primary structure

Secondary structure

Tertiary structure

Quaternary structure

Primary structure refers to the peptide linkage between the amino acids, resulting in long polypeptides chain molecules. Secondary structure refers to increasing the complexity of the polypeptide chain by folding it into pleated sheets, or bending it into a helical shape, like a coiled spring. Numerous and very weak bonds maintain either shape. These bonds are called hydrogen bonds and are found between C=O of one amino acids carboxyl group, and the N-H of another amino acids amino group.

Hydrogen bond

Type of weak bond responsible for secondary structure

Tertiary structure refers to the three-dimensional shape the final protein molecule takes. This shape determines the protein's function. If the protein molecule shape changes, it could lead to a loss of its function. An important bond that helps some proteins retain their shape comes from the sulfur containing amino acids. The sulfur is found in these amino acids as sulfhydryl groups or S-H.. When two sulfur containing amino acids come together in the presence of oxygen, the sulfur's come together to form a disulfide bridge, a very strong bond.

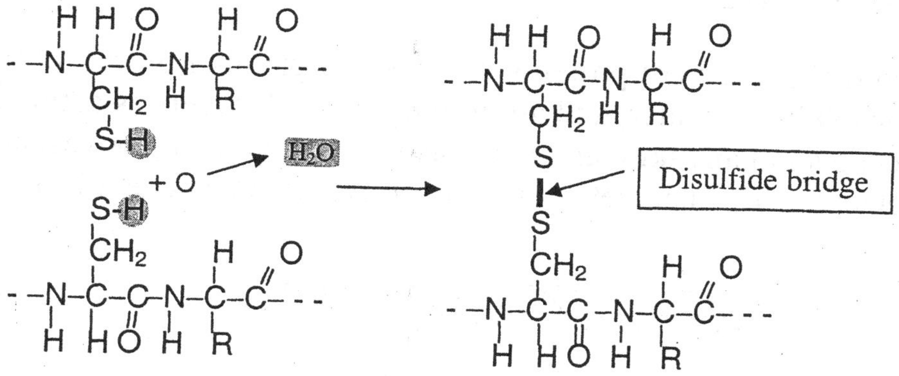

The chemical diagram at top showing disulfide bridge formation:

$$H_2O$$

Disulfide bridge

This change is referred to as denaturation, it is a change in the secondary or tertiary structure but not the primary structure. If the primary structure is changed, the proteins said to be digested, coagulated, or precipitated, and this is always an irreversible change. For example, if an egg is fried, the egg is coagulated and it is impossible to go back to its original form. Getting a permanent, or straightening one's hair is simply an example of a mild denaturation of the protein molecule. In this case it is reversible. Wrapping hair in hot curlers breaks the weak hydrogen bonds, which reform when the curlers cool down, but with temporary curls in the hair. A permanent, is more permanent. In this case the very strong disulfide bridges are broken and reformed in the curled shape, thus giving a more permanent change to the molecule.

Quaternary structure refers to the most complex structure proteins can be found as. This refers to when two or more units of tertiary structure being held together as one molecule. Antibodies serve as an excellent example of quaternary structure. The basic antibody molecule has a "Y" like shape. One of these molecules is considered a monomer, two held together a dimer, and five a pentamer. These molecules are called the immunoglobulins.

IgG
Monomer

IgA
Dimers

IgM
Pentamer

PROTEIN FUNCTIONS

There are two main groups of proteins, fibrous and globular proteins. Fibrous proteins are insoluble in water, and are found in muscle fibers as actin and myosin. Keratin molecules in hair, skin, and nails, as well as feathers, hooves, and horns. Collagen molecules in bone, teeth, and connective tissue, and as fibrin to clot the blood.

Fibrous protein

Globular proteins mainly exist as albumins and globulins. They are water-soluble. Egg white is mostly albumin, albumins are also found in blood, where they bind with lipids to transport them to cells to be metabolized. Globulins are found as the immunoglobulins protecting the body from disease, and as hemoglobin transporting oxygen to the cells. Globulins are found in every living cell as part of the cell membrane, permitting dissolved materials to pass through into or out of the cell. Some globular proteins regulate, as hormones. Examples of hormones are insulin which regulates sugar in the body, and somatotropin which regulates growth. The most important of all proteins are the globular enzymes.

Globular protein

Enzymes

For any chemical reaction to occur, the reactants must be brought together. If the reaction doesn't proceed spontaneously, usually some type of outside help like heat, electric current, or a catalyst, must be added for the reaction to proceed. A catalyst is a substance that speeds up a reaction, but isn't changed during the reaction. Most reactions occurring in living things rely upon a form of organic catalyst called an enzyme. Enzymes end in "ase", and the name usually describes the substrate, or the material the enzyme works on. The enzyme dehydrogenase removes hydrogens. Urease attacks the urea molecule, and so on. The substance that is eventually formed is called the product. Each of these enzymes is highly specific to the substrate it works on.

Let's look at the following analogy:

A problem for you to solve. It is time to get revenge on your professor for making you learn all the terrible knowledge you have been exposed to thus far. If the boulder in the diagram were moved to a certain point, it would roll down the hill all by itself, and destroy the house. There are two ways this could be achieved. See if you could come up with the answer, before you continue reading.

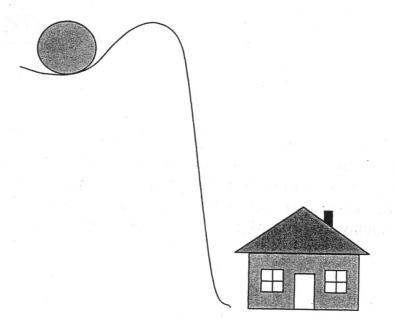

No cheating allowed!

The first way would be to use energy to push the boulder to the top of the hill. The amount of energy required is called energy of activation and is shown below. This reaction now proceeds by itself and the boulder will roll down the hill.

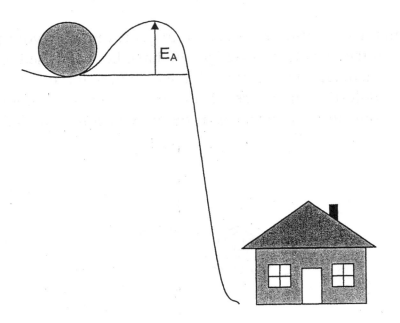

The second way, is similar to the way an enzyme works. The E_A is lowered, in our case, by bulldozing enough of the hill to allow the boulder to roll spontaneously. An enzyme accomplishes this feat by having its unique three-dimensional shape, where it can cradle the substrate perfectly in what we call the active site, so that the reaction proceeds quickly and the enzyme itself is unchanged, and can be used repeatedly.

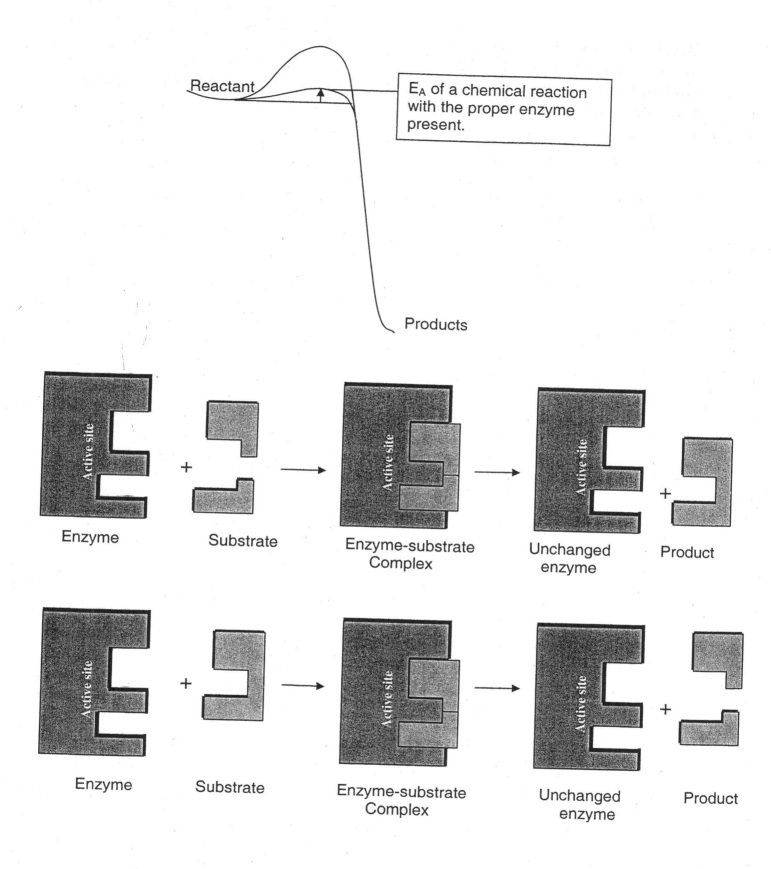

Reactant

E_A of a chemical reaction with the proper enzyme present.

Products

Enzyme + Substrate → Enzyme-substrate Complex → Unchanged enzyme + Product

Active site

Enzyme + Substrate → Enzyme-substrate Complex → Unchanged enzyme + Product

Active site

Because enzymes are complex proteins, they are very delicate molecules, and denaturation, altering its three dimensional shape, can easily occur with environmental changes, such as pH and temperature. These changes can drastically affect how the enzyme works.

INTRODUCTION TO THE CELL

All life forms are composed of units, called cells. The cell, can be described simply as a bag within a bag. The outer bag is the cell membrane, which holds in all the contents. The inner bag is the nuclear membrane which holds the contents of the nucleus. The fluid like material of the cell is called protoplasm. In the nucleus the type of protoplasm is called nucleoplasm, and outside of the nucleus the protoplasm is called cytoplasm.

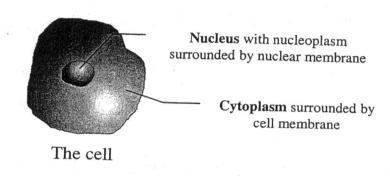

Nucleus with nucleoplasm surrounded by nuclear membrane

Cytoplasm surrounded by cell membrane

The cell

NUCLEIC ACIDS

When a cell is stained with a colored dye, simple chemical neutralization takes place. Basic stains are attracted to, and stain acidic cell structures. Acid stains are attracted to, and stain basic cell structures. When the nucleus or central structure of the cell was first stained, it attracted basic stains, showing scientists that the nucleus was acidic in nature. This acidic material was then given the name nucleic acid.

Most nucleic acids are found in the nucleus of the cell as colored bodies called chromosomes. Each chromosome is composed of many units called genes. A gene is the sequence of DNA that encodes for the synthesis of a protein. Two main types of nucleic acids exist. DNA or deoxyribose nucleic acid, and RNA, ribose nucleic acid. The DNA is the genetic material found in the nucleus of the cell. This DNA controls what an individual organism will look like, and how it will function. It does this by controlling which proteins will be produced by each and every cell of the organism. The RNA's main function is to transport the DNA's information from the nucleus to the site of protein synthesis, in the cytoplasm, and aid in that synthesis.

DNA

DNA like other macromolecules, is composed of building blocks called nucleotides. These nucleotides all contain a phosphate group and an aldopentose, that hold the individual nucleotides together. The aldopentose (deoxyribose) is connected to a cyclical nitrogen containing base.

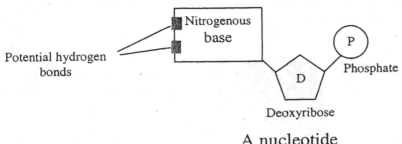

A nucleotide

In DNA there are four different nitrogen containing bases. Thymine and adenine, both will form two hydrogen bonds when on opposite strands, along with cytosine and guanine, both forming three hydrogen bonds when on opposite strands. As a result of these hydrogen bonds, thymine always combines with adenine, and guanine with cytosine.

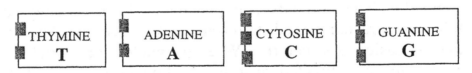

Nitrogen containing **bases**

We can simplify working with these bases by using their first letter, to represent them. A simple polynucleotide would appear as shown below.

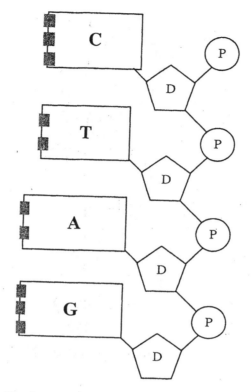

Single stranded DNA polynucleotide

The actual DNA molecule is very long, as much as six feet coiled tightly in each cell. In 1953 the Nobel Prize was awarded to Watson and Crick, who proposed the three-dimensional structure of the DNA molecule. The DNA molecule is shaped like a spiral staircase, with a deoxyribose and phosphates form the railing, and the bases form the rungs, or steps. We call this molecular configuration, a double Helix.

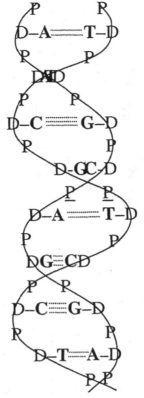

Double stranded DNA

REPLICATION

The DNA molecule is capable of reproducing itself in the cell, with the aid of enzymes, when the cell is ready to replicate. We find a metabolic pool, made up of the building blocks of all the macromolecules, within the cell. When DNA replication is to take place, the double helix begins to unwind. The weak hydrogen bonds break, separating the DNA into two strands. Each strand's nitrogen base, in turn bonds with a complementary nitrogen base found in the metabolic pool of the cell. The end result is a doubling of the DNA. Two molecules, where one existed before. Now the cell can divide, and each daughter cell will contain the exact same molecule of DNA.

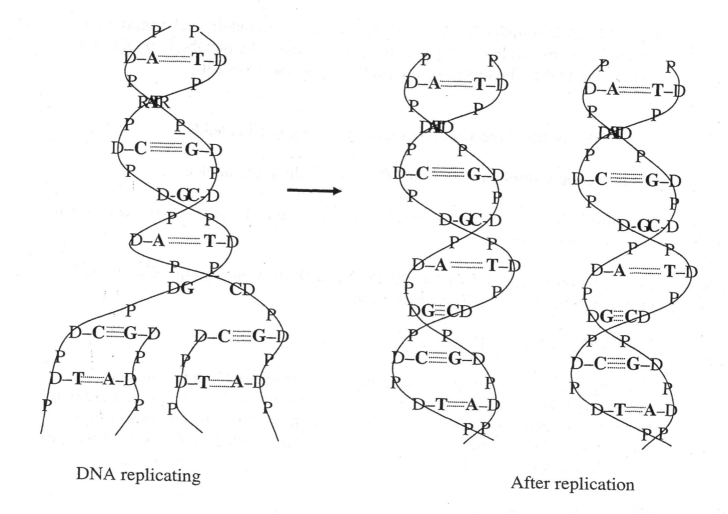

DNA replicating

After replication

RNA

Ribose nucleic acid differs in some ways from the DNA molecule. The nucleotides of RNA contain the sugar ribose in place of deoxyribose, and the base uracil replaces thymine of DNA. RNA molecules are single-stranded, and much smaller than DNA.

| URACIL |
| U |

There are three types of RNA molecules, each with its specific job. Messenger RNA or mRNA, transcribes the message of one gene, from the DNA of the nucleus, and carries it to the cytoplasm. The second type of RNA is ribosomal or rRNA. The ribosome is a structure in the cytoplasm of the cell, where protein synthesis takes place. The ribosome is partially composed of rRNA. The third type of RNA is transfer RNA or tRNA. This RNA transfers each specific amino acid required to synthesize a particular protein, from the metabolic pool in the cytoplasm, to the ribosome, for the protein synthesis to occur.

Summary of the three vital processes involving nucleic acids

1) replication = duplication of the DNA molecule in the nucleus.

2) transcription = message transcribed in the nucleus, from DNA to mRNA which travels to the cytoplasm.

3) translation = mRNA translates to tRNA, with its proper amino acid, to make protein on the ribosome in the cytoplasm.

PROTEIN SYNTHESIS

The sequence of the nitrogen containing bases of the DNA in the nucleus eventually will determine the sequence of the amino acids in the protein (enzyme) to be synthesized. All encoding occurs in groups of three nucleotides, usually identified by their nitrogen containing base. This is usually referred to as a triplet in DNA or a codon in mRNA.

Let's follow an example:

Suppose the partial sequence of nitrogen bases in DNA is ATA CGT. mRNA would be synthesized to correspond to that DNA portion. The DNA would unwind as it does during replication, except in this case, a complementary mRNA portion is synthesized (transcription). The complementary mRNA has the sequence UAU GCA. Each specific mRNA triplet encodes for a specific amino acid, as well as instructions to be begin, or stop the protein synthesis.

The Genetic Code

mRNA codon	Amino acid translation
AAA or AAG	Lysine
AAC or AAU	Asparagine
ACA, ACC, ACG or ACU	Threonine
AGA, AGG, CGA, CGC, CGG, or CGU	Arginine
AGC, AGU, UCA, UCC, UCG, or UCU	Serine
AUA, AUC, or AUU	Isoleucine
AUG	Methionine (start)
CAA or CAG	Glutamine
CAC or CAU	Histidine
CCA, CCC, CCG, or CCU	Proline
CUA, CUC, CUG, CUU, UUA, or UUG	Leucine
GAA or GAG	Glutamic acid
GAC or GAU	Aspartic acid
GCA, GCC, GCG, or GCU	Alanine
GGA, GGC, GGG, or GGU	Glycine
GUA, GUC, GUG, or GUU	Valine
UAC or UAU	Tyrosine
UGC or UGU	Cysteine
UGG	Tryptophan
UUC or UUU	Phenylalanine
UAA, UAG, or UGA	(Stop)

The mRNA attaches itself to the ribosome, and it is the ribosome that moves along the strand of mRNA. The tRNA's contain an important triplet, called the anti-codon, where each tRNA is attached to its specific amino acid, from the metabolic pool in the cytoplasm. Our first triplet of mRNA is UAU. This UAU combines with the specific tRNA anti-codon AUA, attached to the amino acid valine. The next triplet of mRNA is GCA. Which combines with the tRNA anticodon sequence CGU attached to the amino acid aspartic acid. At this point, the aspartic acid, via an enzyme, is linked to valine by a peptide bond, and the protein synthesis continues on like this, until the final triplet which functions to stop the synthesis, thus, finishing the molecule. The amino acid-less tRNA molecules are once again can again combine with their specific amino acid in the cytoplasm, in preparation for new protein synthesis.

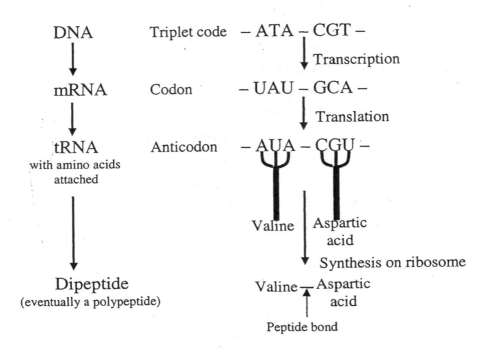

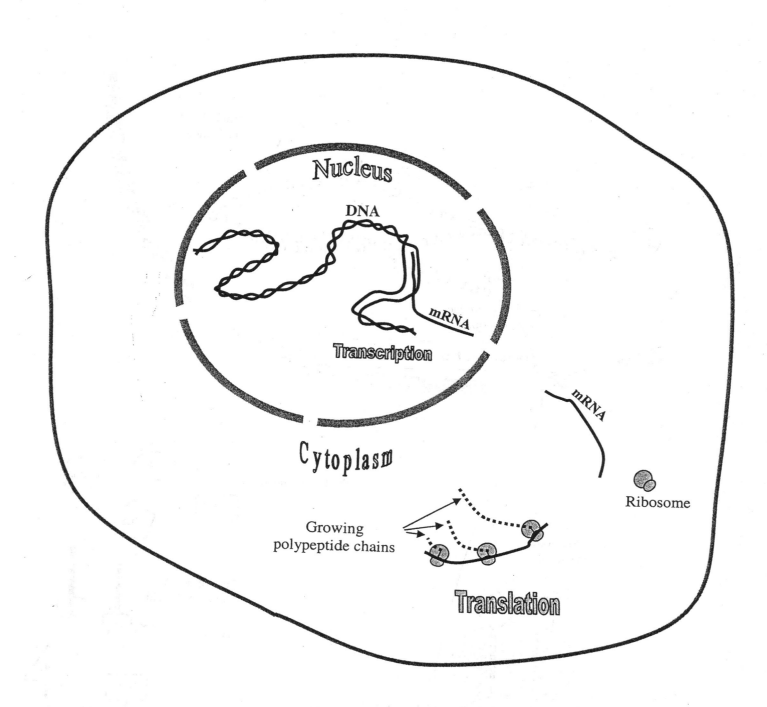

Nucleus

DNA

mRNA

Transcription

Cytoplasm

mRNA

Ribosome

Growing
polypeptide chains

Translation

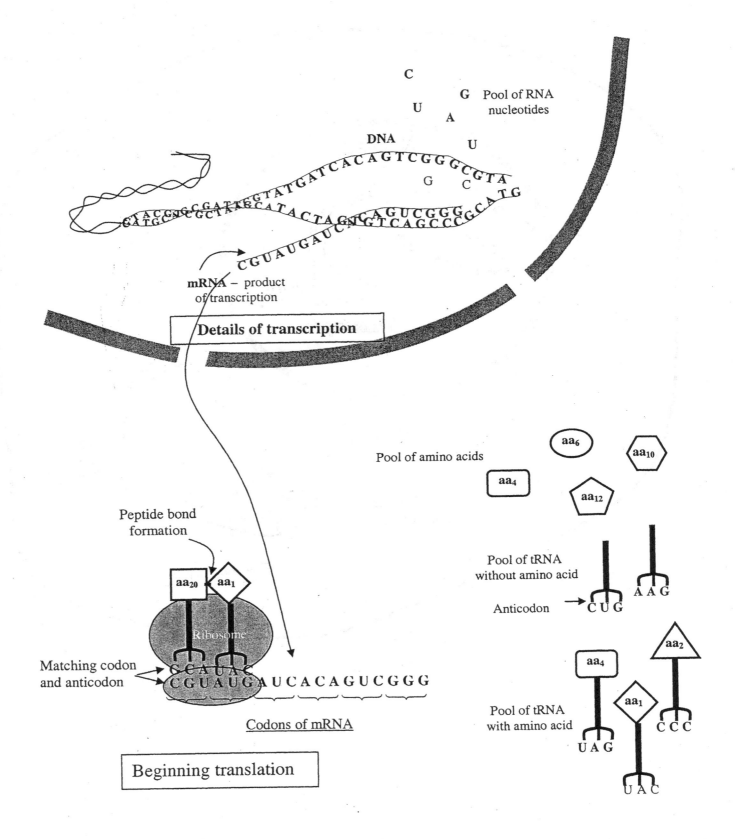

Pool of RNA nucleotides

C

G

U

A

U

G

C

DNA

CTACGTCGCGATTCGTATGATCACAGTCGGGCGTA
GATGCAGCGCTAAGCATACTAGTCAGTCAGCCCGCATG

CGUAUGAUCN

mRNA – product of transcription

Details of transcription

Pool of amino acids

aa₆

aa₁₀

aa₄

aa₁₂

Pool of tRNA without amino acid

Anticodon → CUG

AAG

Peptide bond formation

aa₂₀   aa₁

Ribosome

Matching codon and anticodon
→ CCAUAC
→ CGUAUGAUCACAGUCGGG

Codons of mRNA

aa₄

aa₂

aa₁

Pool of tRNA with amino acid

UAG

CCC

UAC

Beginning translation

90

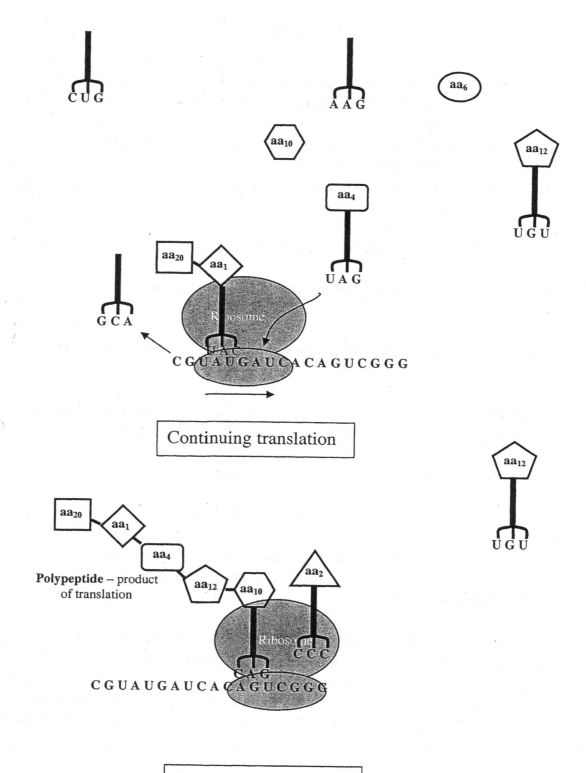

Continuing translation

Polypeptide – product
of translation

Continuing translation

LIFE

So far in this course we have concentrated on the physical and chemical components of life, but we have not talked about what life is. The definition of life can be very complex and confusing in our modern world. When does a human life began? Is it at conception?, or, is it at birth? When does life end? Is it when the brain ceases to function?, is it when the heart stops beating?, or when all body cells die? We don't dare try to answer these questions, but we will discuss the characteristics required for life.

CHARACTERISTICS OF LIFE

1) complex organization = living things are composed of very complex, basic units called cells.

2) metabolism = the use of energy by taking in, processing of nutrients, and the elimination of nutrient wastes.

3) growth and reproduction = through the chemical reactions of metabolism, the living organism can increase in size, as well as replicate itself.

4) responses to internal and external environments.

THE CELL

The cells activities are amongst the most complex workings of anything that humans can imagine. Living things can consist of a single cell, or can be a multicellular organism.

Let's compare a cell to a factory. The factory is enclosed in a building. Raw materials are brought to the loading dock. These materials are made into the product by machines. Energy is brought in, taking the form of electricity and natural gas to operate the machines. The products are warehoused in the factory, and waste materials of the manufacturing process are brought out of the factory to be disposed of. All of these and many other similar activities are going on in the factory, as well as in the cell, all the time.

METABOLISM

Metabolism consists of all the chemical reactions that occur within the cell (organism). It is composed of two subdivisions, anabolism and catabolism. The term anabolism, literally means "to throw up" or, " buildup". The cell synthesizes necessary substances to allow for its growth and functioning, but it does this at the expensive of energy, which is gained from catabolism. This term literally means "to throw down" or, "break down". Almost all of the chemical reactions of metabolism rely upon enzymes to take place.

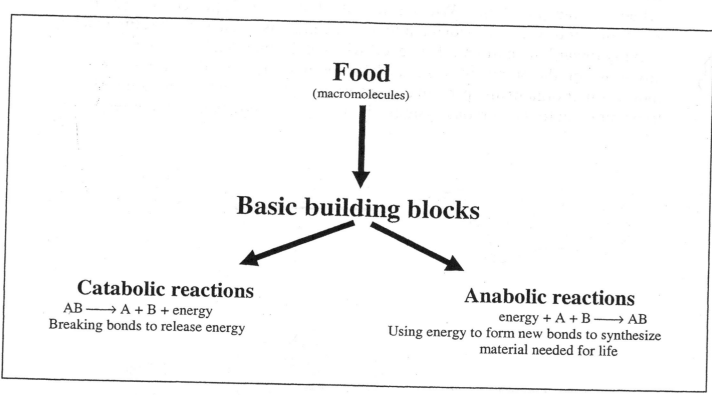

GROWTH AND REPRODUCTION

Growth allows for the addition and repair of structure within the cell (organism), as well as storing nutrients. Assimilation is the term used to describe these events, carried out via metabolism.

Reproduction allows for the cell (organism) to replicate itself, making sure that life continues on. In the individual cell this is carried out through a process called mitosis. In simpler living things, replication is asexual, where the organism simply divides to produce two identical organisms, where one existed before. In more complex organisms, two different, but related organisms recombine their characteristics to form a new organism, containing the genetic materials of each parent. This type of reproduction is said to be sexual.

RESPONSE TO THE ENVIRONMENT

Any change in both the internal or external environment, provides to the cell (organism) what is called a stimulus. The response made, due to the stimulus is called irritability. A simple example is positive and negative chemotaxis meaning "chemical transportation". When a single cell organism is placed in a watery environment to which is added a nutrient, the organism reacts to the stimulus by moving toward the nutrient. However, when an irritant is added to the environment, the organism will react by moving away from the irritant. In multicellular organisms specialized sensory receptors detect the stimuli and transmit them to the nervous system which then determines the proper response.

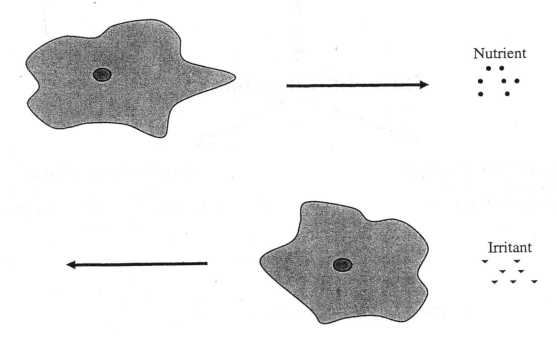

IMPORTANT CELLULAR PROCESSES

For cells to survive, they have to create an internal (intracellular) environment, which is totally different from the external (extracellular) environment. The cell must take in nutrients and dissolved gases, and eliminate wastes. This transportation into and out of the cell, which is accomplished by several processes, that can be divided into two categories. The first of these, rely strictly on natural physical events to take place by themselves, without the addition of energy. These processes are referred to as inactive or passive transport, and include diffusion, osmosis, and filtration. The second category includes active transport, phagocytosis "the process of cell eating", and pinocytosis "the process of cell drinking". These processes require energy in the form of ATP.

All of these cellular processes rely upon membranes for the passage of materials into and out of the cell. The membrane found at the perimeter of the cell is the plasma, or cellular membrane, which is selectively permeable, allowing certain substances to be transported into and out of the cell. The structure of the membrane is based on a fluid mosaic model. It is made of a phospholipid bi-layer, with these phospholipid molecules fluid-like, floating and not bonded to one another. This phospholipid molecule is shaped like a balloon with two strings attached to it.

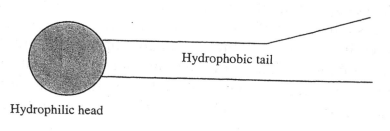

Diagram of a phospholipid molecule

The balloon end of the molecule is said to be hydrophilic "to love water", attracting water molecules, because it is ionic in nature. The string section is covalent, or nonionic, and is said to be hydrophobic "to fear water". Every so often we find a hollow membrane protein molecule, which, either penetrates completely or incompletely through the bilayer from either inside or outside the membrane. These proteins act as gates or channels, through which the materials will pass. Cholesterol molecules are also found in the membrane, they affect the fluidity of the membrane.

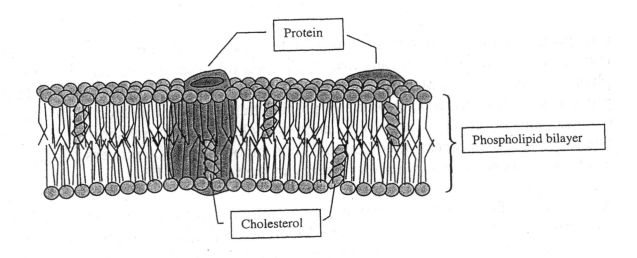

BIOLOGICAL ORGANIZATION

Organisms are either composed of a single cell capable of all the characteristics of life, or they are multicellular. The multicellular organism's organization begins with a group of like cells, which all function to accomplish a specific job. The term for these cells, is a tissue. Different tissues are grouped together, each doing their specific job creating an organ, which is capable of carrying out a more specific job. If we combined different organs together to carry out important life functions, they would be called organ systems. The multicellular organism is composed of all the organ systems working together to maintain life.

Levels of Organization

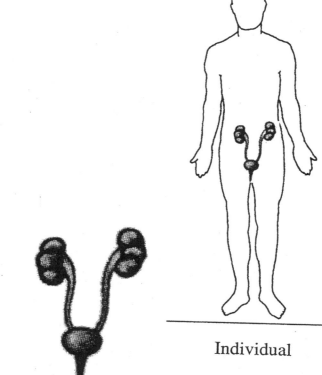

Individual

Organ system level

Organ level

Tissue level

Cellular level

Biological Terminology Made Simple

Biological terms are usually long words containing several syllables. Beginning students often have great difficulty pronouncing these words and consequently not remembering their meaning. With rare exception these terms are composed of word pans which have meaning by themselves. Many of these word parts have wide usage and are common to a large number of biological terms. The meanings of these word parts frequently give clues to the meaning of the term in which they are found. If you can learn these word pans. together with clues from the context of your readings, then you will have an independent word attack skill, which will aid you in both pronunciation and comprehension in the biological sciences. Many of these word pans are joined to one another by short meaningless connectives like -o- in pseud-o-pod or chrom-o-some. This makes the word easier to pronounce. An alphabetical listing of these word pans will follow. Those with a* next to them receive more widespread usage. This list should be saved as reference for future use. The rest is up to you.

A

A*: NO, NOT, WITHOUT.
AB*: AWAY, FROM.
ABI: TO DEPART.
ABYSS: DEEP.
ACARO: TINY.
ACER: SHARP.
ACET: VINEGAR.
ACI: NEEDLE.
ACIN: GRAPELIKE.
ACOU: HEARING.
ACRO: EXTREMES. HEIGHTS, EXTREMITY.
ACTINO: RAYS.
ACU: NEEDLE.
AD*: TOWARD, NEAR, MORE, ADDITION, INTENSE.
ADEL: CONCEAL.
ADEN*: GLAND.
ADIP: FAT.
AER*: AIR.
AESTH: SENSATION.
AFFER: TO BRING.
AGGLUT: TO GLUE ON.

AGGREG: TO COLLECT.
AGGRESS: TO ATTACK
AGRIO: WILD.
AITIO: CAUSING.
AL: PERTAINING TO, ALL, THE.
ALA: WING.
ALB: WHITE.
ALET: WANDERER.
ALG*: PAIN, SEAWEED.
ALIMENT: NOURISHMENT.
ALLAT: AIDED.
ALLASS: TO CHANGE.
ALLEL: ONE ANOTHER.
ALLO: OTHER.
ALLUV:TOWASH.
ALTRI: NOURISHER.
ALVEOL: PITTED.
ALY:UNEVEN.
AMBI*: BOTH, ABOUT, AROUND.
AMBLY: DULL.
AMBUL:TOWALK.
AMEL: ENAMEL.
AMMO: SAND.

AMOEB: CHANGE.
AMPHI*: BOTH, AROUND, ABOUT.
AMPHO: IN BOTH WAYS.
AMPLEX: TO EMBRACE.
AMPLI: TO ENLARGE.
AMYLO: STARCH.
ANA*: UP, EXCESSIVELY, BACK, AGAIN, THROUGH, NO.
ANCON: ELBOW.
ANDRO: MALE, MAN.
ANEM: WIND.
ANGIO: VESSEL, SEED.
ANGUST: NARROW.
ANKYLO: CROOKED.
ANNUL: RING.
ANO:ANUS,UP.
ANOMO: LAWLESS.
ANS: HANDLE.
ANSIO: UNEQUAL.
ANTE: BEFORE, TOP.
ANTI*: AGAINST.
ANTH: FLOWER.
ANTRO: CAVITY.
AP: AWAY, FROM.
APH: AWAY, FROM.

APHIA: TO TOUCH.
APHAN: INVISIBLE.
APEX: SUMMIT.
API: BEE.
APLO: SINGLE.
APO: AWAY,FROM.
APOLE: TO CHOOSE.
APPEND: TO HANG.
AQU: WATER.
ARACHON: SPIDER.
ARBO: TREE.
ARC: BOW.
ARCH*: OLD. PRIMITIVE,
    FIRST.
AREOL: SMALL SPACE.
ARESC: TO DRY UP.
ARG: SILVER.
ARIL: HOOP
ARIST: BEST.
ARKY:NET.
ARO: TO RAISE.
AROL: PROTECTION.
ARRHEN: MALE.
ARTHRO: JOINT.
ASCO: SAC.
ASE*: ENZYME.
ASPER: ROUGH.
ASTA: CRAYFISH.
ASTER: STAR.
ASTRO: STAR.
ATACTO: IRREGULAR.
ATAV: ANCESTOR.
ATHER: THICK, FLUID.
ATHRO: COLLECTIVE.
ATRA: BLACK.
ATRE: IMPERFORATE.
ATRIO: CENTRAL ROOM,
    CHAMBER.
AUDI*: HEAR.

AUG: TO INCREASE.
AULO: TUBE.
AURAL: HEAR.
AURI: EAR.
AURO: GOLDEN.
AUTO*: SELF, SAME.
AUX: INCREASE,
    GROWTH.
AVE: BIRD.
AVI: BIRD.
AX: AXIS, AXLE,
    CYLINDER.

B

BACI: STAFF.
BACT: ROD SHAPED.
BARB:BEARD
BARO: HEAVY WEIGHT.
BASI: STEP.
BASID:BASE.
BAT: BEAT.
BATHMO: DEGREE.
BATHO: HEIGHT.
BATHY-.DEEP.
BENTH: SEA DEPTH"S.
BI*: TWO.
BILI: BILE.
BIO*: LIFE.
BLAST*: GERM, SEED,
BUD, PRIMITIVE CELL.
BLEPH: EYELASH.
BOL*: TO THROW.
BOLET: MUSHROOM.
BOSSE: KNOB.
BOTRY: BUNCH OF
    GRAPES.
BOUS: OX.
BRACH: ARMS,
    BRANCHES.

BRACHY: SHORT.
BRACTE: THIN METAL
    PLATE.
BRADY: SLOW.
BRANCH: GILLS.
BREV: SHORT.
BROCH: LOOP.
BROMA: FOOD.
BRONCH: WINDPIPE.
BRYO: MOSS.
BUBO: GROIN.
BUCC: CHEEK.
BUFO: TOAD.
BULB: GLOBULAR ROOT.
BULL: BUBBLE.
BUNO: MOUND.
BURS: A POUCH.
BUTYR: BUTTER.
BYS: COTTON.

C

CACO: BAD.
CADU: FALLING.
CAEC: BLIND.
CAENO: RECENT.
CAINO: RECENT.
CALC: HEEL SPUR LINE
CALL: HARD.
CALOR: TO BE WARMED.
CALYPTI: COVERING.
CALYPTO: HIDDEN.
CAMBI: CHANGE.
CAMERA: VAULT.
CAMPAN: BELL.
CAMPTO: FLEXIBLE.
CAMPYLO: CURVED.
CAP*: HEAD, TOP.
CAR: FLESH.

CARBO: COAL.
CAPILL: HAIR.
CARCER: PRISON.
CARD: HEART.
CARI: DECAY.
CARPO: FRUIT.
CATA*: AGAINST, DOWN,
    ACCORDING TO.
CAUD: TAIL.
CAUL: STALK, STEM.
CELE: TUMOR.
CENE: RECENT.
CENT*: HUNDRED.
CENTR*: CENTRAL,
    MIDDLE.
CEP*: HEAD, TOP.
CEPTOR*: RECEPTOR.
CER: WAX.
CERC: TAIL.
CERE: BRAIN.
CERV: NECK.
CHAETE: HAIR.
CHAISMA: CROSS.
CHEL: CLAW.
CHITIN: TUNIC.
CHLAMYD: CLOAK.
CHLORO: YELLOW.
CHOL: BILE.
CHONDRO: CARTILAGE.
CHORD*: CORD, SPINE.
CHORIO: SKIN.
CHORO: PLACE.
CHROM*: COLOR.
CHRON:TIME.
CHRYSO: GOLDEN.
CIDE*: TO KILL.
CIL*: HAIR.
CIRC*: CIRCLE AROUND.
CIRR: CURL.

CLAST: BREAKER,
    DESTROYER,
    DISSOLVER.
CLAV: CLUB.
CLEISTO: CLOSED.
CLIMAX: LADDER.
CLINE: SLANT BED.
CNID: NETTLE.
CO*: WITH, TOGETHER.
COM*: WITH, TOGETHER.
CON*: WITH, TOGETHER.
COC: COILED, HELICAL.
COCCUS: BERRY.
COEL*: HOLLOW.
COEN: COMMON.
COL: TO INHABIT.
CONDYL: KNUCKLE.
CONI: DUST.
CONTRA*: OPPOSITE.
    AGAINST.
COPRO: FECES.
CORM: TRUNK.
CORN: HORN.
COROLL: CROWN.
CORON: CROWN.
CORP*: BODY.
CORTEX: BARK.
COPTIC: BARK.
COSTA: RIB.
COTYL: CUP.
COXA: HIP.
CRAN: SKULL.
CRENA: WEDGE.
CRINE: TO SECRETE,
SEPARATE.
CRUST: SHELL.
CRYO: FROST.
CRYPT: HIDDEN.
CRYST: ICE.

CTEN: COMB.
CUSP: POINT.
CUTI: SKIN.
CYANIN: DARK BLUE.
CYCL: CIRCLE AROUND.
CYS: BLADDER.
CYTE*: CELL.

D

DACRY: TEAR.
DACTYL: FINGER
DE*: BY REASON OF,
    DOWN, AWAY.
DECA*: TEN.
DECI*: TENTH.
DEMA: BODY.
DEMI*: HALF.
DEMO*: PEOPLE.
DENDR: TREE.
DENT: TOOTH.
DERM*: SKIN.
DESIS: BINDING.
DET: BOUND.
DEUT*: SECOND.
DEX: TO THE RIGHT.
DI*: TWO, INTENSIVE.
DIA*: THROUGH.
DIGIT: FINGER.
DIPLO*: DOUBLE.
DIS*: TO STAND APART.
DODECA: TWELVE.
DONT: TOOTH.
DORS*: BACK.
DROME*: TO RUN,
    COURSE.
DUC*: TO LEAD, TUBE.
DUPLI: DOUBLE.
DUR*: HARD, TO ENDURE.
DYNAM: POWER.

DYNIA: PAIN.
DYS*: BAD.

E

E*: OUT OF, WITHOUT.
EC*: OUT.
ECHINO: SPINE.
ECIOUS: HOUSE.
ECO: HOUSEHOLD.
ECTO: OUTER.
EF*: OUT.
EL: TO ROLL.
ELAI: OIL.
ELATER: DRIVER.
ELECTRO: AMBER.
ELEUTHERO: FREE.
ELYTRI: SHEATH.
EMBOL: THROWING IN,
    WEDGE.
EMESIS: VOMITING
EMIA: IN BLOOD.
EN*: IN.
ENCEPHALO: BRAIN.
ENCHYMA: INFUSION.
ENDO*: INNER, WITH.
ENT*: WITHIN.
ENTER: INTESTINE.
EO: DAWN.
EPI*: UPON, TOWARDS.
EQUI: EQUAL.
ERG: WORK.
ERR: TO WANDER.
ERS: YOUNG.
ERYTH: RED.
ESTH: SENSATION.
ETH: CUSTOM.
ETHNO: NATION.
ETRON: BELLY.
EU*: GOOD, TRUE.

EUTHY: STRAIGHT.
EURY: WIDE.
EX*: WITHOUT.
EXO*: OUTSIDE.
EXTRA*: BEYOND.

F

FAB: BEAN.
FAC: TO MAKE.
FACI: FACE.
FARINA: FLOUR.
FASC: BAND, BUNDLE.
FAV: HONEY COMB.
FEBRILL: FEVER.
FENEST: WINDOW.
FER*: TO BEAR.
FERR: IRON.
FIL: THREAD, FIBER,
    BAND.
FISS: CLEFT.
FIST: PIPE.
FLAGEL: WHIP.
FLAV: YELLOW.
FLEX: TO BEND.
FLO: FLOWER.
FLOCC: A LOCK OF
    WOOL.
FLUVI: RIVER.
FOLI: LEAK.
FOLLI: SMALL SAC
FONTA: FOUNTAIN.
FORAM: OPENING.
FORE*: FRONT, BEFORE.
FORI: DOOR.
FORM*: SHAPE.
FOVE: DEPRESSION.
FRON: FOREHEAD.
FUC: SEAWEED.

FUGE*: FLEE.
FUND*: BASE.
FUNG: MUSHROOM.
FURC: FORK.
FUSC: BROWN.
FY*: TO BECOME.

G

GALA: MILK.
GAMO: MARRIAGE.
GANGLI: TUMOR.
GASTR: STOMACH.
GELAT: TO CONGEAL.
GEMIN: DOUBLE.
GEN*: CHIN, OFFSPRING,
    RACE, DESCENT,
    KNEE, BEGET.
GEO*: EARTH, WORLD.
GER*: TO CARRY.
GERA: OLD AGE.
GERM: BUD.
GESTA: TO BEAR.
GIGA: GIANT.
GING: GUMS.
GLADI: SWORD.
GLAN: ACORN.
GLEN: SOCKET.
GLIA: GLUE.
GLOB: ROUND.
GLOM: BALL, WIND-UP.
GLOS: TONGUE.
GLOT: TONGUE.
GLU: SWEET, SUGAR.
GLUT: BUTTOCKS, GLUE.
GLYCO: SWEET, SUGAR.
GNATH: JAW.
GOG: TO MAKE FLOW.
GON: SEED.

GORGO: TERRIBLE
GRADE: STEP.
GRAM: PICTUIRE
GRAMIN: GRASS.
GRAN: GRAIN.
GRAPH: TO WRITE.
GRAVI: HEAVY.
GUAN: DUNG.
GUST: TO TASTE.
GYMN: NAKED.
GYNE: WOMAN.
GYPSO: CHALK.
GYR: CIRCLE.

H

HABIT: TO INHABIT,
    APPEARANCE.
HAD: UNSEEN.
HAL: SALT.
HALO: SEA.
HAM: HOOKED.
HAPLO: SIMPLE.
HAPT: TO TOUCH, TO
FASTEN.
HARM: TO ARRANGE, TO
    FIT.
HAUST: TO DRAIN.
HELI: SPIRAL.
HELIO: SUN.
HELO: MARSH.
HELMIN: WORM.
HEM*: BLOOD.
HEME: BLOOD.
HEMI*: HALF.
HEP: LIVER.
HERB: GRASS.
HERP: REPTILE.
HETERO*: DIFFERENT.

HEX: SIX.
HIBERN: WINTRY.
HIPPO: HORSE.
HIST*: TISSUE.
HOLO*: WHOLE.
HOMO*: SAME, MAN.
HUMOR: FLUID.
HY: "Y" SHAPED.
HYAL: GLASS.
HYBRID: TO CROSS.
HYDRO: WATER.
HYGRO: WET.
HYLO: WOOD
HYMEN: MEMBRANE
HYPER*: MORE, HIGHER,
    ABOVE.
HYPH:WEB.
HYPNO: SLEEP.
HYPO*: BELOW, LOWER,
    LESS.
HYSTER: COMING
    AFTER. WOMB.

I

IASIS: CONDITION.
ICOSA: TWENTY.
ICTH: FISH.
ID: DISTINCT, PERSONAL.
IDEO: TO SEE.
IDIO: PECULIAR TO.
ILEO: ILEUM.
ILIO: FLANKS.
IM: IN, NOT.
IN*: WITHIN, NOT.
INFER: BENEATH.
INFRA: BELOW.
INHIB: TO RESTRAIN.
INGUIN: GROIN.
INTEG: WHOLE.

INTER*: BETWEEN,
    AMONG.
INTRA*: WITHIN.
INTRO: ENTRY.
IODO: VIOLET.
ION: GOING.
IR: IN, NOT.
IRI: RAINBOW:
ISA: LIKE, SAME.
ISCHI: HIP.
ISI: PLANT.
ISM*: CONDITION OF,
    THEORY.
ISO*: LIKE, SAME.
ITIS*: INFLAMATION OF.
IZE: TO TREAT.

J

JACULAT: TO SHOOT.
JECT: TO TOSS.
JEJ: EMPTY
JUG*: JOINING, MATING,
    TO YOKE.
JUNC: JOINING, MATING,
    TO YOKE.
JUNG: JOINING, MATING,
    TO YOKE.
JURA: MOUNTAINS.
JUV: YOUTHFUL.
JUXTA: CLOSE TO.

K

KAINO: NEW.
KAK: FAILURE.
KAL: ASH, COVERING,
    HUT.
KARY: NUT, NUCLEUS.

KAT: DOWN.
KEN: EMPTY.
KERA: CORNEA, HORN.
KILO*: THOUSAND.
KIN: TO MOVE, MOTION.
KLEISTO: CLOSED.
KLEPTO: TO STEAL.
KLINE: TO SLOPE.
KONIO: DUST.
KOPO: FATIGUE.
KYMO: WAVE.
KYO: PREGNANCY;
KYPHO: BENT.

L

LAB: LIP.
LACER: TO TEAR.
LACINI: FLAP.
LACRI: TEARS.
LACT: MILK.
LACUN: CAVITY.
LACUS: LAKE.
LAGEN: FLASK.
LALIA: SPEECH.
LAM: LAYER.
LAMELL: SMALL PLATE.
LAMIN: THIN PLATE.
LANIA: TO TEAR TO
    PIECES.
LAPARO: LOIN.
LAPID: STONE.
LAPPA: BURR.
LAPS; SLIPPING.
LARV: GHOST.
LARYNG: LARYNX.
LATER: SIDE.
LATI: WIDE.
LATIC: LIQUID.
LAV: WASH.

LECITH: EGG-YOLK.
LECTO: CHOSEN.
LEIO: SMOOTH.
LEMMA: SKIN.
LENT: LENTIL.
LENTIG: FRECKLE.
LEPID: SCALE.
LEPTO: SMALL, SOFT.
LEV: TO LIFT, LEFT.
LEUC: WHITE.
LEX: WORD.
LIEN: SPLEEN.
LIG:TOBIND.
LIGN: WOOD.
LIGUL: LITTLE TONGUE.
LIMB: BORDER.
LIME: THRESHOLD.
LIMI: MUD, HUNGER.
LIMN: LAKE.
LIN: THREAD.
LIPO: FAT.
LIRE: FURROW.
LISS: SMOOTH.
LITE: STONE.
LITH: STONE.
LITTOR: SHORELINE.
LOB: FLAP.
LOC: PLACE.
LOCU: COMPARTMENT.
LOGO: WORD.
LOGY*: STUDY OF.
LOPHO: CREST.
LOR: THRONG.
LOX: OBLIQUE.
LU: TO WASH.
LUCI: LIGHT.
LUMI: LIGHT.
LUN: MOON.
LUTE: ORANGE-YELLOW

LYGO: SHADOW.
LYMPH: WATER.
LYO:TOLOSE.
LYSIS: DISSOLUTION OF.
LYTTA: MADNESS.

M

MACE: TO SOFTEN.
MACH: TO FIGHT.
MACRO*: BIG.
MACULA: SPOT.
MADRE: MOTHER.
MAL: JAW, BAD, POOR,
    EVIL.
MALACO: SOFTEN.
MALL: HAMMER.
MAMM: BREAST.
MANDIB: JAW.
MANO: LOOSE.
MARG: EDGE.
MARSUP: POUCH.
MASTIC: TO CHEW.
MASTID: BEAST.
MASTIG: WHIP.
MASTO: BREAST.
MAXIL: JAW.
MED: MIDDLE, PITH.
MEGA: VERY LARGE.
MEIO: SMALLER
MEL: HONEY.
MELA: BLACK.
MEN: MONTH.
MENING: MEMBRANE.
MENS: MIND.
MENT: CHIN, MIND.
MERI: PART.
MERO: PART.
MESO*: MIDDLE.

META*: BEYOND, CHANGE.
METABOL: CHANGE.
METE: BEYOND, CHANGE.
METER*: MEASURE.
METO: BEYOND, CHANGE.
METR: WOMB.
MICRO*: SMALL.
MICT: MIXED.
MILLA: THOUSANDTHS.
MILLI: THOUSANDTH.
MIM: MIMIC.
MIO: LESS.
MITO: THREAD.
MIXO: MINGLE.
MNEM: MEMORY.
MOD: MEASURE.
MON*: ONE.
MONT: MOUNTAIN.
MORPH*: FORM, SHAPE.
MOTOR: MOVEMENT.
MUC: MUCUS.
MULT*: MANY.
MUR: WALL.
MUTA*: CHANGE.
MY: MUSCLE.
MYC: FUNGUS.
MYELO: MARROW.
MYRIO: NUMBERLESS.
MYX: SLIME.

N

NANO: DWARF.
NARC: NUMBNESS.
NASO: NOSE.
NAT: BORN.

NATAR:TO SWIM.
NAUPLI: SHELLFISH.
NAVI: SHIP.
NECRO: DEAD.
NECTO: SWIMMING.
NEMA: THREAD.
NEO: NEW.
NEPHR: KIDNEY.
NEPIO: INFANT.
NEUCL: KERNEL.
NEUR: NERVE.
NEUT: NEITHER.
NIMB: CLOUD.
NIT: NITROGEN.
NOCT: NIGHT.
NOD: KNOB.
NOM: NAME.
NON: NO.
NORM: RULE.
NOSO: DISEASE.

O

OB*: TOWARD, AGAINST.
OBTUS: BLUNT
ODCCIP: BACK OF HEAD
OCCLUS: TO CLOSE
OCHRO: PAL
OCTA: EIGHT.
OCULO: EYE.
ODE: WAY.
ODMIA: STENCH.
ODONT: TOOTH.
ODYNIA: PAIN.
OID*: LIKE,EGG, FORM.
OIK: HOUSE.
OLE: OIL.
OLFACT: SMELL.
OLIG: FEW.

OMA: TUMOR.
OMNI: ALL.
ON: BEING
ONT: BEINGS.
ONY: NAIL.
OO: EGG.
OOPHORON: OVARY.
OPE: HOLE.
OPERC: LID.
OPIS: BEHIND.
OPSI: LATE.
OPSIS: SIGHT.
OPTHAL: EYE.
OPTIC: SIGHT.
ORAL: MOUTH.
ORB: ROUND.
ORCHID: TESTICLE
ORGAN: INSTRUMENT.
ORN: BIRD.
ORO: MOUTH.
ORTHO*: STRAIGHT, NORMAL.
OS: MOUTH.
OSIS*: CONDITION, INCREASE.
OSM: SMELL.
OSTEO: BONE.
OTO: EAR.
OV: EGG.
OXY: OXYGEN.

P

PACHY: THICK.
PALEON: OLD.
PALLIUM: MANTLE
PALP: TO TOUCH, SOFTLY, TO STROKE.
PALPE: EYELID.

PAN*: EVERYWHERE, ALL.
PAP: NIPPLE, PIMPLE.
PAR*: TO PRODUCE, BEAR.
PARA*: WITH, BESIDE.
PARI: WALL.
PARTH: VIRGIN.
PATH*: DISEASE, TO SUFFER, FEELING.
PAUCI: FEW.
PECT: CONGEALED, COMB, BREAST.
PED: FOOT.
PEDO: SOIL, GROUND.
PELAG: SEA.
PELLI: SKIN.
PELOR: MONSTROUS.
PELT: SHIELD.
PELVI: BASIN.
PEND*: HANGING.
PENIA: POOR, LACK OF.
PENTA: FIVE.
PEP: TO DIGEST.
PER: THROUGH, EXCESSIVE.
PERI: AROUND.
PERON: FIBULA.
PERV: PASSABLE.
PETAL: LEAF.
PETR: STONE, ROCK.
PHAGE: TO EAT.
PHALLO: PENIS.
PHANIC: TO SHOW.
PHAO: LIGHT.
PHARM: DRUG.
PHASE: STAGE. STEP.
PHENO: TO APPEAR.
PHIAL: BOWL, CUP.
PHIL: LOVING, FOND OF.

PHYLAXIS: PROTECTION.
PHLEB: VEIN.
PHLO: INNER BARK.
PHYLSIS: ERRUPTION.
PHOB: FEAR.
PHON: SOUND
PHORE: BEARING
PHORESIS: TO SWEAT
PHOS: LIGHT.
PHOT: LIGHT.
PHRAGMO: FENCE.
PHREN: DIAPHRAGM, MIND.
PHTHORA: CORRUPTION.
PHYCO: SEAWEED.
PHYG; FLIGHT.
PHYLA: RACE.
PHYLAC: GUARD
PHYLL: LEAF.
PHYMA: SWELLING.
PHYSA: BLADDER.
PHYSIS: NATURE., GROWTH.
PHYT: PLANT.
PIA: TENDER.
PIG: TO PAINT.
PILE: CARP.
PILI: HAIR.
PINNA: WING.
PINO: DRINK.
PISCI: FISH.
PISO: PEA.
PLAC: PLATE.
PLAGIO: SIDEWAYS.
PLAN: FLAT, WANDER.
PLANT: SOLE OF FOOT.
PLASIA: TO MOLD.
PLASM: FORM.
PLASTO: FORMED.
PLATY: FLAT.

PLECT: TWISTED.
PLEGE: SHOCK.
PLEIO: MORE.
PLESIO: NEAR.
PLEURA: SIDE.
PLEX: INTERWOVEN.
PLIC.TO FOLD.
PLIO: MORE.
PLOTO: FLOATING.
PLUM: FEATHER.
PLURI: MORE.
PNEUM: TO BREATHE
POD: FOOT.
PODIC: RUMP.
POGON: BEARD.
POIETIC: TOMAKE.
POIKILO: VARIOUS.
POL: AXIS
POLIO: GREY.
POLY*: MANY.
PONS: BRIDGE.
POR: CHANNEL.
PORPHYR: PURPLE.
PORTA: GATE.
POST*: AFTER, BACK.
POTEN: POWERFUL.
PRE*: BEFORE, IN FRONT OF.
PRIM*:MOST, IMPORTANT, FIRST, HIGHEST.
PRIO: SAW.
PRO*: BEFORE, FOR. FIRST, START.
PROCT: ANUS.
PROTERO: FORE.
PROTO: FIRST.
PROX: NEXT TO, NEAREST.
PSEUD*: FALSE.
PSOR: ITCH.

PSYCH: SOUL, MIND.
PTER: WING, FEATHER.
PTOM: DEAD BODY.
PTOSIS: A FALLING.
PTY: TO SPIT, SALIVA.
PUB: MATURE.
PULMO: LUNG.
PULO: CUSHION, DUSTY.
PUNCT: POINT.
PUPA: PUPPET.
PURPUR: PURPLE.
PYCN: THICK.
PHY: GATE.
PYO: PUS.
PYR: FEVER, BURNING.
PYRE: FRUIT STONE,
    PEAR.
PYX: FOX.

Q

QUAD: FOUR, SQUARE.
QUANT: AMOUNT.
QUASI: AS IF, JUST LIKE.
QUERUL: TO COMPLAIN.
QUIESC: TO BE STILL.
QUIN: FIVE.

R

RACEM: BUNCH.
RACHIS: SPINE.
RAD: RAY, ROOT.
RADU: TO SCRAPE.
RAM: BRANCH.
RAN: FROG.
RAPH: NEEDLE.
RE*: AGAIN.
RECEPT: TO RECEIVE,
    RESERVOIR.

RECESS: WITHDRAWN.
RECLIN: TO LEAN.
RECT: STAIGHT.
REFLEC: TO TURN BACK.
REFLEX: TO TURN BACK.
REM: OAR, ROW.
REN: KIDNEY.
REPLIC: TO FOLD BACK.
REPT: TO CRAWL.
RESIL: TO LEAP BACK.
RESP: TO BREATHE.
REST: RESTORATION,
    ROPE.
RETE: NET.
RETR: BACKWARDS.
RHABD: ROD.
RHAGE: TO FLOW.
RHAM: BEAK.
RHAPY: STITCHING.
RHE: TO FLOW.
RHIG: COLD.
RHIN: NOSE.
RHIZ: ROOT.
RHOD: RED.
RHYNCH: SNOUT.
RIG: STIFF.
RIM: CLEFT.
RIS: LAUGHTER:
RIV: STREAM.
ROD: TO GNAW.
ROST: BEAK.
ROTAT: WHEEL.
RRHEA: TO FLOW.
RUB: RED.
RUBIG: RUST.
RUG: WRINKLE.
RUPT: A BREAK.

S

SACCH: SUGAR.
SACRO: SACRUM.
SACRUM: SACRED.
SAGITT: ARROW.
SALT: TO LEAP.
SANGUI: FLOOD.
SAPHEN: CLEAR.
SAPRO: DECAY.
SARCO: FLESH.
SAUR: LIZARD.
SAX: ROCK.
SCAB: ROUGH.
SCAL: LADDER.
SCALP: CHISEL.
SCAP: STEM, STALK.
SCAPH: BOAT.
SCHIZ: SPLIT.
SCLER: HARD.
SCOLE: WORM.
SCOLO: STAKE.
SCOP: BRUSH.
SCOPE: TO VIEW.
SCROT: BAG.
SCUT: SHIELD.
SCYPH: CUP.
SEBUM: WAX.
SECRET: TO SEPARATE.
SECT: TO CUT.
SECUND: FOLLOWING.
SEGMENT: PIECE.
SEIO: TO SHAKE.
SEISM: SHAKING.
SELACH: SHARK.
SELEN: MOON.
SELL: SADDLE.
SEMA: SIGN.
SEMI*: PARTIAL.
SENES: TO GROW OLD.

SENT: TO FEEL.
SEPA: TO SEPARATE.
SEPSIS: PUTREFACTION.
SEPT: SEVEN, PARTITION
SERE: TO PUT IN A ROW.
SERI: RANK.
SERO: SERUM.
SERR: SAW.
SET: BRISTLE.
SIAL: SALIVA.
SIB: KIN.
SICC: DRY.
SIDERO: IRON.
SIER: GREY.
SINIST: LEFT.
SINU: CURVE, GULF.
SIPHON: TUBE, REED.
SITO: FOOD.
SKELET: DRIED, HARD.
SKIO: SHADE.
SKOTO: DARKNESS.
SOL: SUN.
SOLEN: CHANNEL.
SOMA: BODY.
SOR: HEAP.
SORB: TO SUCK IN.
SPADIC: PALM, LEAF.
SPAN: TO DRAW.
SPANO: SCARCE.
SPASM: TENSION.
SPATH: BROAD BLADE.
SPATUL: SPOON.
SPEC: APPEARANCE,
    MIRROR.
SPECI: KIND.
SPERM: SEED.
SPHAG: MOSS.
SPHERE: ROUND.

SPHINCT: BINDER.
SPHYGM: PULSE.
SPIC: SPIKE.
SPINA: THORN, SPINE.
SPIR: COIL.
SPIRACUL: AIR HOLE.
SPLANCHN: ENTRAIL.
SPLEN: SPLEEN.
SPONDYL: VERTEBRA.
SPORAD: SCATTERED.
SPORE: SEED.
SPURI: FALSE.
SQUAM: SCALE.
STALSIS: CONSTRICTION.
STAMEN: WARP
STAPE: STIRRUP.
STASIS: STANDING.
STEG: COVER.
STEL: PILLAR.
STELL: STAR.
STENO: HARROW.
STERC: DUNG.
STERE: RIGID, SOLID.
STERN: BREAST.
STETH: CHEST.
STHENO: STRENGTH.
STIGMA: POINT, MARK.
STILL: DROP.
STIP: STALK.
STOMA: MOUTH.
STRAT: LAYER.
STREP: TWISTED.
STRIAT: GROOVE.
STROMA: BEDDING.
STROPHE: TURN.
STYL: PRICKER, PILLAR.
SUB*: UNDER.
SUCC: SAP.

SUCR: SUGAR.
SULC: FURROW,
    GROOVE.
SUPER: OVER.
SUPIN: BENT BACKWARDS.
SUPRA: ABOVE.
SUR: OVER.
SUTUR: SEAM.
SYLV: FOREST.
SYM: TOGETHER.
SYN: WITH.
SYNAP: UNION.
SYNDESIS: TO BIND
    TOGETHER.
SYSTAL: TO DRAW IN.
SYZYG: UNION.

T

TACHY: QUICK.
TACT: TOUCH.
TAEN: RIBBON.
TALO: ANKLE.
TANGO: TO TOUCH.
TANY: TO STRETCH.
TAPE: CARPET
TARS: SOLE OF FOOT
TARTAR: ACID SALT.
TAS: A CLASP.
TAUR: BULL.
TAUT: THE SAME.
TAX: ARRANGEMENT.
TECT: ROOF, COVERING,
BUILDER.
TEG: COVERING, TILE.
TEL: FAR, COMPLETE,
    END.
TELA: WEB.
TELEUT: COMPLETION.

TEMPO: TEMPLES.
TEN: TO HOLD.
TEND: TO STRETCH.
TENT: TO FEEL.
TENTO: TENT.
TENU: SLIGHT.
TERA: MONSTER.
TERC: THIRD.
TERE: BORER.
TERES: ROUNDED.
TERG: BACK.
TERM: END.
TERMI: WOOD WORM.
TERMO: LIMIT.
TERN: THREE EACH.
TERR: EARTH, DOMAIN.
TERT: THIRD.
TEST: SHELL, TESTICLE.
TETAN: STRETCHED.
TETRA: FOUR.
TEXT: FABRIC.
THALAM: CHAMBER.
THALASS: SEA.
THALL: YOUNG SHOOT.
THALP: WARM.
THANA: DEATH.
THEC: CASE.
THELE: TEAT.
THELY: FEMALE.
THERM*: HEAT.
THERO: SUMMER.
THESO: DEPOSIT.
THIG: TO TOUCH.
THIO: SULFUR.
THORA: CHEST.
THREP: TO NOURISH.
THROMB: CLOT.
THRYPTO: TO ENFEEBLE.
THYLO: POUCH.

THYM: THYMUS.
THYR: OBLONG, SHIELD,
    DOOR, WAND.
TIBI: SHIN.
TID: TIME.
TIGR: SPOTTED.
TINC: DYEING.
TIPHO: POOL.
TMEN: TO CUT.
TOCO: BIRTH, OFFSPRING.
TOMENT: STUFFING.
TOME: CUTTING.
TON: TENSION, PRESSURE.
TOPO: PLACE.
TOR: SWELLING.
TORM: SOCKET.
TORN: TO TURN.
TORS: TO TWIST.
TOT: ALL.
TOX: POISON, BOW.
TRACH: WINDPIPE, NECK.
TRACT: TO DRAW, TO
    PULL, REGION.
TRANS*: TO PASS BY,
    BEYOND, TO LEAP
    OVER,CHANGE
    SHAPE.
TRAUM: WOUND.
TREM: TO TREMBLE.
TREPH: TO NOURISH.
TRI: THREE.
TRIB: BURR, TO RUB.
TRIC: TO KNIT.
TRICH: HAIR.
TRIP: THREEFOLD,
    TRIPLE.
TRITO: THIRD.
TRIV: CROSS-ROAD.
TROCH: WHEEL,

PULLEY, RUNNER.
TROP: KEEL, TURN.
TROPH*: NOURISHMENT,
    BROOD, TO FEEL.
TROPO: MODE.
TRYM: HOLE.
TRYPAN:TO BORE.
TRYP: TO RUB DOWN, TO
    GRIND DOWN.
TUB: PIPE. TUBE.
TUBER: HUMP.
TUM: TO SWELL.
TUN: COATING.
TURB: WHIRL.
TURG: TO SWELL.
TUTAN: PROTECTION.
TYCH: CHANCE.
TYL: KNOB, CALLUS.
TYMP: DRUM.
TYP: PATTERN.
TYR: CHEESE.

U

UL: THE GUMS.
ULN: ELBOW.
ULO: SCAR.
ULTI: END.
UMB: SHADE.
UMBIL: NAVEL.
UMBO: SHIELD, BOSS.
UMBRA: SUN-SHADE.
UN*: WITHOUT, NOT.
UND: TO RISE IN WAVES,
    BILLOWY.
UNG: NAIL, CLAW, HOOF.
UNI: ONE.
UR: URINE.
URC: SMALL PITCHER.

URET: URETERS.
URN: JAR.
URO: TAIL.
UTE: LEATHER BOTTLE.
    WOMB.
UTRI: SMALL BAG.
UV: GRAPE.

V

VACC: COW.
VACU: EMPTY.
VAG: WANDERING,
    INDEFINITE.
VAL: TO BE STRONG.
VALL: VALLEY
VALV: FOLD.
VANN: FAN.
VARI: TO CHANGE.
VARIC: DILATION.
VARIO: SMALLPOX.
VAS: VESSEL.
VECT: CARRIER, BEARER.
VEGET: TO ENLIVEN.
VEL: COVERING.
VELU: VELVET.
VEN: VEIN, POISON.
VENT: BELLY.
VERD: GREEN.
VERM: WORM.
VERNAC: INDIGENOUS.
VERNAL: OF THE SPRING.
VERNI: VARNISHED.
VERRUC: WART.
VERS: TO TURN.

VERTEB: TURNING, JOINT.
VERT: TOP, WHORL.
VESI: BLADDER.
VESP: WASP.
VESPE: OF THE EVENING.
VESTIB: PORCH.
VESTIG: TRACE.
VESTIT: GARMENT.
VETER: BEASTS OF
BURDEN.
VI: LIFE.
VIA: WAY.
VIBR: TO VIBRATE.
VIBRIS: NOSTRIL. HAIR.
VICAR: DEPUTY.
VICIN: NEIGHBOR.
VILLI: SHAGGY HAIR.
VINC: BOND.
VIR: POISON, GREEN.
VISC: BOWELS.
VISCO: VISCOUS.
VIS: TO SEE.
VIT: LIFE.
VITEL: YOLK.
VITR: GLASS.
VIV: LIVING, ALIVE.
VOC: VOICE.
VOLT: TIME.
VOLUN: WILL.
VOLV: WRAPPER.
VOM: PLOUGHSHARE.
VORT: VORTEX.
VULV: VULVA.

X

XANTHO: YELLOW.
XESIS: SCRAPING.
XIPH: SWORD.
XYL: WOOD.
XYRO: RAZOR.
XYSMA: FILINGS.

Y

YL*: MATERIAL.
YPSIL: GREEK LETTER "Y"

Z

ZA: VERY.
ZEA: CORN.
ZELO: ZEAL.
ZEM: SOIL.
ZEMIA: TO LOSE.
ZEO: TO BOIL.
ZEUGO: JOINED.
ZOA: ANIMAL.
ZOL: TO LEACH.
ZONE: GIRDLE, AREA.
ZOO: ANIMAL.
ZOSTER: GIRDLE.
ZYGO: MATE, YOKE.
ZYGOMA: A BAR.
ZYME: FERMENT.